The Fortunes *at* War

The Fortunes at War

TONY FOOT

The Book Guild Ltd

First published in Great Britain in 2017 by
The Book Guild Ltd
9 Priory Business Park
Wistow Road, Kibworth
Leicestershire, LE8 0RX
Freephone: 0800 999 2982
www.bookguild.co.uk
Email: info@bookguild.co.uk
Twitter: @bookguild

Typeset in Minion Pro

Printed and bound in the UK by TJ International, Padstow, Cornwall

ISBN 978 1911320 494

British Library Cataloguing in Publication Data.
A catalogue record for this book is available from the British Library.

To: A man from Norfolk, Sergeant James Rudling
1ˢᵗ Battalion, The Rifle Brigade (my great grandfather)
and to all 'Rifles' since.

Prologue

During the first half of the 19ᵗʰ century there was growing suspicion of Russian ambition in the Balkans and the Holy Land. For Catherine the Great back in the 18ᵗʰ century and Tsar Nicholas I in the 19ᵗʰ, expansionism was, as well as territorial gain, a religious duty ostensibly to protect Christian holy places throughout the eastern Mediterranean from Ottoman (Turkish) interference and influence.

Russia was spreading down the shores of the Black Sea and into Crimea. The whole area was a confusion of competing races and religious faiths. In the French view, Russian belligerence, although suffering setbacks borne out of ill-equipped and poorly trained peasant soldiers facing determined Turkish opposition, might, if unchecked, give Russia control of all lands surrounding the Black Sea and offer easy access into the Mediterranean. Religion was superficially the catalyst as Britain and France prepared to intervene and help the Turks protect those same religious sites from Russian domination. Militarily, and for politicians such as Lord Palmerston ever keen to promote Britain as a world power, Russia threatened Britain's control of India. France, under Napoleon III saw the impending conflict as the obvious means to not only curb Russian ambition but a convenient opportunity to re-kindle some of the greatness that had been achieved under Napoleon Bonaparte. Russia on the other hand, was anticipating a repeat of its successes against the French invasion of its territory just as it had done in 1812.

Britain had not been involved in a major war since Waterloo.

Its army was small, poorly equipped but always colourful on the parade ground! Worse still, it was led by highborn but not always competent officers. Of Raglan's original force bound for the Crimea only the Rifle Brigade had experienced recent active service (in South Africa.) But if the war achieved anything it did lead to reform. Its many shortcomings were soon to be highlighted by *The Times* correspondent William Russell's twice-weekly bulletins informing the public of the sufferings of the men and the mismanagement of the campaign.

The French, unlike their allies, were better in many respects. They had seen recent active service in Algeria and were better led, certainly better fed and equipped.

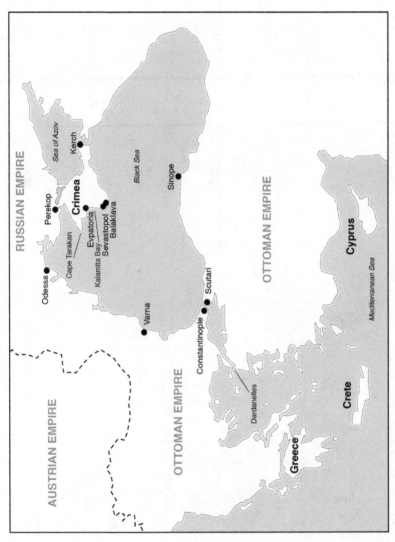

Sevastopol and the Crimea

Sevastopol Harbour

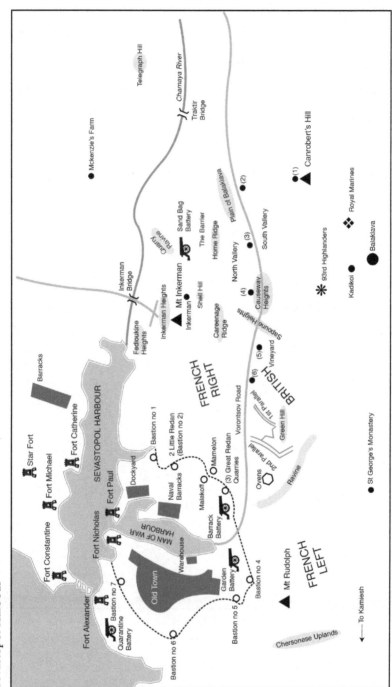

1

We had landed at Dover in the January of 1854 from service in Cape Colony, South Africa, and were billeted at the Western Heights Barracks. In March we travelled by train and then took up quarters in Clarence Barracks, Portsmouth.

I had hoped to get home to see my parents in Hampshire around this time but that would have to wait for a month or two, as we were kept very busy. We were preparing for something, but quite what that was still remained for some time the subject of rumour and gossip. Our 2nd Battalion, who in recent years had spent a lot of time in Canada, had arrived back in the country at Portsmouth in May 1852, then moved on to their barracks in Kent. They had then been chosen to represent our regiment, the Rifle Brigade, at the Duke of Wellington's funeral in November of that year. This had not though turned out to be quite the respectful and sombre duty they and thousands of spectators had expected. For two months before the Duke's funeral, London had experienced very heavy rain. Many districts had been flooded. Water mixed with sewage and every kind of waste. The stench had apparently been foul. To complete an already miserable scene, the hearse sank into the mud around Pall Mall and it took dozens of men and horses to pull it clear.

Like us in the 1st Battalion, they were billeted in Clarence Barracks before their next overseas duty.

The talk in the sergeants' quarters of my battalion was of the way matters seemed to have rushed on apace with the other companies. We had seen for ourselves around the streets near the barracks that wives and children of the 2nd Battalion, many of them Canadians, had just been left destitute before adequate provision could be made for them. They could, as a last desperate resort, appeal for help to the local Union workhouse!

My company commander had told us a story that his father had told him about the burying of French dead after the battle of Waterloo. It seems that just as one particular body was about to be carted away, it was discovered that the soldier was a woman. Not wishing to be parted from her presumably conscripted husband, she had disguised herself and joined the ranks alongside him. This, our officer told us, was not unlike something that had occurred in the 2nd Battalion. Not wishing to become a burden on the ratepayers of Portsmouth, a rifleman's wife had dressed in an exact copy of the uniform and had even acquired a Brunswick rifle. He, or rather she, made it to the deck, only to be discovered minutes before the steam-driven screw ship was due to leave harbour. It turned out that her daring and initiative was rewarded by her not being put ashore. So off she went to, we were later told, a place called Scutari near Constantinople, along with her husband and about 800 officers and other ranks. She was only one of a handful of wives allowed to accompany ordinary soldiers.

Rifleman Williams, never short of an opinion, had his rather sour say on the devotion of wife to husband: "If that's love and marriage, give me madness any day."

At one of our morning parades, we had been told that we would be sailing east to fight the Russians. There did seem, however, to be some doubt as to why we were going and, regardless of what we had been told, who the opposition would really turn out to be. Soon even more rumours were flying around. Especially as soldiers from other regiments were still being drafted in to our battalion to bring it up to strength. This usually meant only one thing: somewhere there was a war, or one about to take place. At the end of March, war was officially declared. But where and who it would be against was yet to be confirmed. Would it be against the Russians or, like forty years before, the French, we would be fighting?

Newspaper reports and talk around the town was at fever pitch for teaching the Russians a lesson, yet reasons seemed to be less hot. Old soldiers and sailors around the docks still did not trust the French.

I got into conversation in a public house with an old sailor who had served under Admiral Nelson at the Nile and Trafalgar.

"You can't trust 'em. Revolutions every five minutes and conquered half of Europe. They'll be up to something, you mark my words, soldier boy. If they do turn out to be on our side then you watch your back!"

I couldn't really add much to the conversation. The French though must have fought well to achieve what they did. We would all just have to wait and see what happened.

As several companies returned to barracks one warm, sunny, late Spring day from practising skirmishing skills across a hill to the north of Portsmouth, for the benefit of soldiers new to the Brigade, rifleman Williams observed, "Don't matter who it is. We all know who'll be the daft bastards crawling from rock to rock with shot and shell pouring down on our heads. It won't be natives like South Africa with old guns and spears behind them rocks. No difference if they're Russkis, Frogs or Turkeys, they'll have weapons like ours and bleedin' great big field guns and mortars!"

We had learned from the newspapers and some of our officers that last year there had been fighting around the River Danube following an invasion by the Russians. An English and French fleet had been sent to the Dardanelles. Then, it was reported, the Russian fleet had destroyed Turkish ships at Sinope. Closer to home, the 2nd Battalion of my regiment had also set sail after marching through Portsmouth with their band playing them on to their ship, *HMS Vulcan*. How these events were connected, if they were, was still not very clear. Yet if what our colonel had told us proved accurate, then we would also be leaving soon, though where was still vague. We would not necessarily be going in the same direction as the other battalion. While we had been sweating in South Africa they had no doubt been freezing in Canada.

Although I am a Hampshire man, I didn't know the town of Portsmouth at all and I do like to get to know the local terrain.

The town occupies mainly the southeastern corner of Portsea Island. Most of the northern part contains fields and farms with the occasional house straddling the road. There is one bridge off the island taking the road to the mainland and on towards London. There are some fortifications just below the bridge to protect the harbour and dockyard. To my soldierly eye, these defences looked barely adequate to stop a determined attack from the north, though the most likely attacker from past experience would be our new ally – the French. On top of the gently sloping hill were the rotting timbers of a semaphore station. Messages in the days of Nelson could be sent in minutes to the top of this Portsdown Hill on to Butser Hill near Petersfield and from hill to hill to their lordships in the Admiralty in London. Fog probably slowed things down a bit though!

Across the island there are a few scattered settlements and at the water's edge in the south, Southsea Castle and the formidable-looking Round Tower protecting the harbour entrance.

Portsmouth, as we had entered the town by train, was described by one of our officers, Lieutenant Axelby, as a grim place.

There were the genteel residences, large houses with servants, then other comfortable dwellings occupied by naval officers and in total contrast to these was the squalor of the poor, as I discovered when, with a fellow sergeant, I set off to explore. There was the high street with many shops and varying types and quality of entertainment. Across the town were several barracks, many drinking establishments and brothels to render appropriate services.

Around the part of the town known as 'The Hard', sailors, soldiers, beggars and loose women filled the narrow streets. Small children played in filthy alleys and courts. The lack of drainage, overcrowding, poverty and drunkenness probably feeding disease and a noticeable discontent.

As we prepared to walk down one of its streets, a constable called us over. "Best steer clear of here, lads. There's better places for the sort of entertainment you could be looking for. Look at him standing in the shadows of the doorway."

We followed his gaze. Standing in the gloom of the doorway was a young woman dressed in a shawl and the shabbiest of dresses. Just behind her glowered a heavily built man dressed in loose shirt, yellow waistcoat and black, heavily woven trousers held up by a wide leather belt with a huge brass buckle.

"Give her a few pennies for her services three would probably be enough but try and cheat her and he'll have a knife at your throat. Then he'll knock her about to show her who's in charge and take most of the money."

We quickly moved on and after a drink or two of a very passable dark beer in 'The Dolphin' on the high street we returned to barracks.

From what we had seen of the town, it seemed to attract all sorts of characters. How appropriate; I later discovered the town was the birthplace of Mr Charles Dickens, whose books I knew were full of characters of every type of human being and their vices.

***

In town there were agricultural workers from all over Hampshire and Dorset, camp followers of army and navy, deserted wives, widows, the unemployed, the unemployable, the disabled, ex-soldiers and sailors, deserters and vagrants.

Many had come in search of work, but apart from the dockyard, a few shops and domestic service, Portsmouth seemed to have little else to attract it.

There was a police force, but it was outnumbered and paid too little to do or want to do much. A blue jacket had told me, as I asked about my new surroundings in a bar just beyond the dockyard walls, "They're not to be trusted. They keep bad company and slip 'em a shilling and they'll look the other way or walk off rather than break up a fight. There are some parts of town they don't bother to even venture to."

In June, Captain Fortune, my company commander, confirmed during one of our regular morning parades that we would soon be leaving for the eastern Mediterranean. Then it was to be on and into the Black Sea. Lord Raglan, he told us, the one-armed veteran of the battle of Waterloo, was to command an English force against the Russians.

Not long after being given this information, we were marched down to the dockyard to board the 2,245-tonne *SS Orinocco*, a steam-ship with sails. As far as the eye could see there were lines of marching men. In the harbour, ships of every size and type were swallowing men and supplies. I stood on the deck of our new floating billet as riflemen clattered up the gangplanks. Men seemed to be quite relieved that at long last we would soon be under way.

***

There were grins, laughter, slaps on the shoulders and the occasional jokes. Corporal Knighton probably summed up the general feeling when he remarked as he passed me, "Off on our adventure at last, Sergeant Finch. Glad to be going. Sooner we're there, the sooner we're back!"

Leaning against a rail, I wondered how many of the thousand or so officers and men in the battalion would be returning.

Fighting in South Africa had been arduous enough but the Kaffirs or Xhosas we had been up against had only been armed, as Williams had said, with spears and old elephant guns. General Cathcart had been given the task of bringing order to Cape Colony again, following raids by the Xhosa and their Khoikoi allies who stole cattle and frightened local settlers. I found out later that they also wanted lands returned to them that had been given to settlers from England, to the Boers and to a friendly local tribe called the Fengu who had helped the settlers. It was not our job though to question orders, just to carry them out. We pursued the Xhosa, covering several hundred miles and our army defeated a force that included 7,000 mounted tribesmen, under their leader Moshesh. Not long after, their chiefs asked for peace, which was achieved after more cattle were confiscated and even more of their land was handed to tribes who had helped us, and to new settlers. Victory does not always bring fairness!

The Russians, according to yet more rumours, were certainly likely to be better trained and better equipped than those African tribesmen in the Cape.

There would definitely be many thousands of them. They would also be familiar with the local territory and be aware now that war had been declared that we were on our way. Of some comfort to us though was being told that of all the battalions about to take up the fight, mine was the only one to have seen any active service since Waterloo, nearly forty years before. We also had a reputation for being able to operate in small, independent groups. What I had noticed in South Africa was that most other regiments seemed to lack the ability to easily adapt according to the terrain. Not too surprising perhaps, if you're in a bright red tunic, or that the ranks of the English Army have been drawn in recent years from the town whereas once upon a time they were country-bred and more used to hills, rivers and forests. Recruits from the countryside, on the other hand, seemed more at home among the trees, hills and valleys. Riflemen were also specially trained to move quickly, silently and without being seen. We moved in skirmish line to outflank and surprise the enemy and pour accurate fire into them. Our dark green, or rifle green, uniform enabled us to adapt quickly to whatever country we were in.

Thoughts of the likely fighting to come soon passed as our officers directed the sergeants in each company to get the men below. How though would the eight rifle companies that made up the battalion cram below decks? We had experienced enough discomfort on the way to South Africa two years before. From the size of our transport it was only too obvious that this was about to be repeated, as living conditions were going to be extremely cramped. Worse still was being told that meals would have to be taken on deck.

There was just not enough space for tables and chairs. I hoped for good weather and calm seas.

I fell into conversation with one of the crew of the former mail steam packet and must have shown such an interest in the workings of the craft that he later took me on a tour of the boat, as well as giving me a range of facts whether I wanted them or not.

"She's over three hundred feet long from figurehead to taffrail and has a breadth of nearly seventy-one feet between the paddle boxes. And we usually carry over 20-odd 24-pounders to defend ourselves. We normally have a crew of over one hundred, 400 tonnes of coal, and can sleep about 150 passengers. There are ladies' and private cabins now taken up by your officers and they'll dine well in our dining salon. In normal times it would serve dinner for about 120 passengers. On this top deck you'll find four lifeboats, a mailboat, two cutters and a large dinghy to take 200 if we flounder," he said, with some pride.

"That'll be a problem then," I said, "if we hit anything. Let's hope your captain knows the way. One *Birkenhead*'s quite enough!"

I did notice later that whenever we appeared to be steaming too close to land a man was stationed on a ledge above the paddle-box. He was held in place by a harness as he repeatedly swung a lead above his head and cast it far from the boat to take depth soundings. Perhaps we would be spared hitting rocks like the *Birkenhead* after all.

***

My companion showed me below deck. We entered a noisy but well-ventilated engine room. There were two engines with double cylinders, each just a little smaller in height than me. Each of the eight boilers had three furnaces, which, according to my new friend, could evaporate water into steam at the rate of 9,000 gallons each hour. Not that I really understood what it all meant, though I guessed it was enough to power the paddle wheels through the water at about seven knots.

I did manage to walk into a couple of pipes that flared open roughly at the height of my shoulders and then disappeared above my head into the ceiling.

"What are they for?" I asked.

"That's for the captain to call instructions down to the engine room. Full ahead, slow, stop or whatever."

This was certainly a different world to the ones I had experienced on the parade ground or when chasing tribesmen across the Cape.

Not that everything went that cordially between sailor and soldier during our outward voyage; as crewmen rushed to tend the shrouds to increase or reduce sail to assist the engines, it was almost impossible for them not to crash into riflemen walking or lounging on deck.

As men of the *Orinocco* climbed the rigging, we often heard them singing to make their tasks go all the easier.

> *'Away upon her distant course,*
> *A thousand miles from land,*
> *She flings aloft a smoky trail*
> *By circling breezes fann'd;*
> *In flowing triumph thro' the air*
> *To spread o'er oceans face*
> *The glory of our world-formed folk,*
> *The Anglo-Saxon race.*
>
> *'Her huge revolving paddle wheels*
> *Proclaims her wat'ry way;*
> *On each advancing wave they leave*
> *A scar of foaming spray.*
> *Her fires emit a steady blaze*
> *Unquenched across the seas*
> *Which once a myst'ry bay beyond*
> *The Gates of Hercules!'*

It could have been worse for us though as I had noticed Nelson's old flagship, *Victory*, in the harbour. There were even a few very old warships still being used as prison hulks further up the harbour.

Old Walter Langridge, from my village had served on *HMS Royal Sovereign* at Trafalgar and had spun us village boys exciting, if lurid, tales of the battle.

His ship, a one-hundred-gun three-decker had been the first to come under fire, exchanging broadside for broadside. She lost her main and mizzen masts and the foremast was also badly damaged. All rigging had been shot away. *Royal Sovereign* was so badly damaged that she had to be towed home after the battle. Over five hours of fighting left nearly fifty of the crew dead and almost a further one hundred wounded, including Walter. He was pleased to tell us he had left half a leg somewhere off Cape Trafalgar.

After a drink or two, he would roll up his left trouser leg and show us the stump just below the knee to frighten us. Walter's stories of grape and chain-shot cutting main masts as well as sailors in half had served to put me off the navy. There are no back doors on warships. If it goes down, so does its crew. With any luck, on land if all else fails we can always retreat.

At least we did not have to roll out of hammocks on an old man o' war; although some riflemen did have to struggle in and out of their's on the *Orinocco*. I was luckier in having a palliasse, filled with straw. It was, however, a losing battle trying to keep my greatcoat and uniform dry on the continuously wet deck.

We sailed out from the shelter of Portsmouth harbour and other problems soon became all too apparent. Most of the time smoke from the funnels and the constant presence of coal-dust meant we were continually half-blinded and dirty. This was regardless of efforts to keep ourselves reasonably clean. Food, too, also had more than its fair share of tiny, black grit and when the wind got up, smoke and seaspray added their own flavours to our meals. A number of soldiers were also seasick and threw up some of their rations, which also, when the ship rolled, would be blown back on the deck if we were lucky, or on us if we weren't. Before long we also lost two men to cholera.

Boredom soon became part of our daily routine. Some men played cards, a few chess, others played draughts and backgammon in between kit cleaning. Officers, too, appeared no less bored at the in-activity our cramped conditions forced us to endure.

Odd wagers were made as to who could swim the quickest between our ship and the nearest French vessel; Lieutenant Clifton just beating Captain Fortune to the prize of a case of champagne. Men of the new draft were kept a little busier; they were ordered to practise rifle drills. As men in the Rifle Brigade, we were justly proud of the speed and accuracy with which we could load, fire and reload even the Brunswick rifle: twice or more in a minute and still hit the target!

We passed Gibraltar, which looked like a large slice of upturned pork pie; a barren rock with ships crowding around its base like a sow with her piglets. On the 29th July, we reached the Dardanelles, which was crammed with French ships. Then, on to Constantinople and our first real glimpse of the exotic East. We landed two days later just to the north of that city.

Cholera though was certainly continuing to be a problem. The spread of the disease had led to the landing of half our battalion at a town overlooking the entrance to the Bosphorous. Four days later on the 10th of August, the remaining four companies were also landed. The fresh, Black Sea breeze and clear blue skies did not, however, cancel out the spread of cholera, but at least we had a brief respite from cramped ship-board conditions.

Our band was ordered to play at the British Embassy and, on 17th August, we could hear them playing below our camp; however, this could not relieve the air of boredom that was once again setting in and paralysing not just us, but all the other regiments in the area.

***

Cholera during August would claim nearly thirty men in the battalion, including a sergeant and colour sergeant. By the end of the month, we were back on board after burying the victims of the disease.

We then spent a couple of very hot days getting used to a new rifle: the Minié. It had a 39-inch barrel and four rifling grooves, which made it much more accurate than our previous weapon. It had a large calibre, 0.702-inch, and even at one thousand yards the conical bullet could smash up to 4 inches into the trunk of a pine tree. It was certainly a big improvement on the rifle the Brigade had been using since about 1836. Even the old stagers in the battalion had found the Brunswick cumbersome to use, not particularly accurate and too prone to misfire. The bayonet for the Minié, or sword as we called them in the Brigade, was triangular in cross-section and had a blade that was 17 inches long.

Some of the men, including me, took the opportunity to visit Constantinople. It reminded me of a very, very hot London. Opulent houses and richly dressed men with elegantly clothed women, who lounged on divans displaying their very ample bosoms. This scene contrasted with the filthy gutters and uncared for streets in other parts of the city full of bars, brothels, beggars and poorly dressed prostitutes offering all manner of delights. But as the sick-list grew, other less welcome souvenirs of visits to their rooms grew as well.

"Leave them be," I warned a little group of curious riflemen as they ventured close to one colourfully-draped apartment. "It won't be just a possible discharge from the army that you'll pick up here," I added.

***

On 1st September, yet more on the sick-list had to be taken to the hospital at Scutari. Our flagging spirits were raised when we cheered on to our ship the man who had commanded our battalion in South Africa. General Cathcart also brought a present for each man.

The next day we took in tow two transports loaded with artillery pieces and proceeded out of the Bosphorous. All went well until the towrope snapped. The following day, towing just one of the transports, we tried again.

We reached Varna, which, according to what we had heard, was a well-appointed place for the whole army to prepare for its final destination, the Crimea. The main fleet though had just sailed.

As we sailed in, rifleman Williams drew my attention to some strange-looking dark shapes in the water that were just bobbing up and down.

"What do you make of those, sarge?" he asked.

I took a boathook from one of the ship's boats and, as we drew nearer to what I had first thought were empty kegs or pieces of canvas, began to prod at them. One rolled over and we saw the bloated face of a man. There must have been about another thirty or so of them.

"Cholera victims," I said, disgusted at the way they had been treated.

The next day we caught up with the rest of the fleet. The mood was generally low and our band played stirring music while we lay at anchor. Officers from the 2nd Battalion and their guests were welcomed on board.

***

After a very short time ashore where we wandered through yet another squalid town, stinking due to its open sewers that were cooking in the hot summer sunshine, we returned to our floating quarters. Parts of the town still showed signs of a great blaze in early August that had destroyed thousands of boots and tons of food stores.

The *Orinocco* sailed on across the Black Sea. The rest of the fleet, I counted about five hundred of them in four or five lines, was all around us. Steamships and various naval ones all pouring out steam and clouds of dark smoke high into the sky. At night, ships' lanterns twinkled like the stars above. But of the enemy there was no sign at all, not a sail, spar or hint of smoke.

Our only excitement on board the ship during our passage was a fire; fortunately, it did not spread to the store where our ammunition was kept. So quickly had the matter been dealt with that the men in the transport we were towing did not know about the incident until we eventually landed in the Crimea and told them about what could have been a disaster, instead of a narrow escape.

As we approached the site selected for landing, we could just make out some scattered farm buildings a little beyond where we were about to land. The ground around, though flat, also looked rather marshy.

The battalion was told to prepare for going ashore. Small boats filled with soldiers, others pulling barges, began to land men all around the bay.

***

Blue jackets, some half-naked, were standing waist-deep in water apparently enjoying not only the spectacle of soldiers unloading from boats but also carefully helping individual soldiers on to dry land. They were in very high spirits, singing, laughing and joking the whole day long. Muscular arms eased me from the flat-bottomed boat that, along with many others, was transferring my company to the beach from our anchorage in Kalamita Bay.

"There, sarge, not a drop of sea-water on your fine uniform," he said, as he handed me rifle and various pouches of equipment.

It was very slow progress and we spent most of the day, Thursday 14th September, shifting stores and equipment to the shingle-covered shore. We began piling it up into great heaps while we waited for wagons to carry it off.

"Where are the bloody wagons, sarge?" asked rifleman Raynor, waving his arms at the mountain of goods on the beach.

"More like bleedin' Calamity Bay," was rifleman Williams' jaundiced comment, as everything seemed to be going from a crawl to a dead stop.

By mid-afternoon, the beach was crowded with soldiers, horses, artillery and stores. All around, men were starting fires as they prepared to boil water for tea attempting to ignore the vast quantities of ammunition, food and other material all around them.

"Well, that's it, sergeant," exclaimed Captain Fortune in a rather exasperated tone. "Any chance we had of surprising the Russians has long since gone. Look at us – stores as high as a house, horses and men all across the beach and not exactly quiet with bugles and bands soundin' off everywhere. Spot us and hear us miles away, and now news of our arrival will be in Sevastopol long before we are."

"How far is it to that town, sir?" I asked.

"About thirty miles and, according to the French, not the flattest of ground once we do clear here," he replied. "Look," he said, "one of the Frenchies has drawn me a little map. We're about here, and that," he said, jabbing the small square of paper with his cheroot, "is where we're headed, the naval port of Sevastopol."

2

That first night we slept out in the open as the rain poured down. No tents had been sent ashore. Word was, there just hadn't been time to land them. They were sent ashore the next day but for some unknown reason, an order was given for them all to be recalled to the ships. This action, naturally, was not unnoticed by every soldier left to fend off the weather the best way he could.

"What did I say, a bleedin' calamity. Rain, rain and more bleedin' rain. I could have stayed at home if I had wanted rain," said Williams as it dripped off his shako, down his nose and began to form a small puddle in his greatcoat as he sat cross-legged, his back leaning against some boxes.

Men kept warm as best they could by using wood from some of the boats that had brought us ashore. At least we were able to keep boots, socks, shirts and blankets reasonably dry by wrapping them in groundsheets. This was the present that each man had been given by General Cathcart when he had come aboard the *Orinocco*. Some of the men cut a round hole in the middle of their sheet then put it over their heads to keep the rain off. The General had been our commander in South Africa. He was now in command of the 4th Division in the campaign against the Russians.

After the general confusion and delay following our landing, some order was finally introduced and the whole army prepared to march off in divisions.

I was instructed to lead a small patrol in skirmish order to check our left flank. During the night, shots had been fired at what were believed to be Cossacks. As dawn broke, we moved left and forward with about ten or twelve paces between each rifleman. In the distance, we could just make out a small party of horsemen; perhaps they were the same Cossacks who had caused such a stir during the night. They seemed to be short, tough-looking fellows with what appeared to be sheepskin hats and a variety of tunics. They had almost certainly driven off the cattle we had seen grazing just above the beach where we had eventually landed. They were also probably responsible for the fires blackening the walls of farm buildings and cottages beyond the bay area. They made no effort to attack and kept just beyond the range of our rifles.

As we returned to camp to report on the lie of the land, other probing patrols with cavalry escort were sent out; their main task was to secure wagons from the local population to carry our stores.

It proved difficult for the infantry to keep up with their cavalry escort without running. The cavalry doubtless wanting to exercise their mounts after so long at sea, rather than keep a slow pace for the ease of the foot soldiers. Soon the infantry were seen to be scrambling through the marshes that bordered the bay. When they returned to camp we noticed they were limping and suffering from very sore ankles. A few of them just flopped to the ground, unable to walk another step, and were so badly injured they had to join the ranks of the sick and those men who were eventually conveyed to one of the ships and back to the hospital at Scutari.

***

After yet more delays, but now equipped with wagons bartered from local Tatar merchants, the allies were finally able to move. The army was spread over many miles. Drawing a three-day ration of 4½ pounds of meat and biscuits and with full water canteens, we prepared to take position. The French moved off separately from our force and were about four miles away from us. They had the advantage of being on the advancing force's right with the sea in and no doubt comforting, view. Our army occupied the left of the move forward, which after the earlier reconnaissance looked to cover rougher ground a little later on in the march. At first, the landscape was green, pleasant and easy going but this soon gave way to gulleys and hills.

As the army advanced on the Monday following our landing in the bay with the 2nd and 3rd Divisions forming the allied centre, it was an incredible spectacle. The sun glinting on the thousands of helmets and bayonets. Bands too were playing to encourage the men forward.

To the left as they headed south were the Light, 1st and protecting the rear and extreme left flank, the 4th Division with my battalion taking the main covering role. We had, though, always prided ourselves on being in the thick of the fighting and not way behind. Although, looking to our left and ahead we seemed to be the first to have attracted the attention of the enemy. Off we set in skirmish order and as we spread out across the gently rising ground, we noticed a group of wagons moving to the northeast of us. A detachment of Light Brigade cavalry was called up to intercept and hold them.

Captain Fortune, who had been watching the progress of our skirmish line and was probably wondering why we had stopped, ran quickly towards us. Perhaps thinking we had run into trouble, he had rushed up with a half-company of riflemen behind him.

"Everythin' all right?" he asked.

In front of us were about twenty men, women and children, all excitedly pointing towards the southwest. Eventually we managed to calm them down, perhaps covering them with our rifles helped. Some other officers joined this motley collection. Between the broken English of two or three of the men on the wagons and Captain Fortune's French, we gathered they had left their farms, preferring the open road to being caught between two opposing armies. Parties of Cossacks were harassing villages, dispersing cattle, horses and mules and setting fire to farms. Smoke hung in swathes all around. These people declared they were very pleased to see us; they were Tatars who had no particular love for the Russians. Once these people had controlled the whole of the Crimea, but gradually the Russians had seized and taken over much of their land. They now hoped that the presence of the allies and the defeat of the Russians would soon see their lands returned to them. Tatars still remained in Sevastopol, but they risked being shot as spies.

The leader of this particular group was a man of about fifty years of age. He said that the town was heavily defended on the north side of the harbour. The main defensive position, Star Fort, to the north of the main part of Sevastopol could not be taken, he confided.

Our army would need to march south and then turn west across the uplands that overlooked the town. Then they could attack the southern approaches to Sevastopol. The Russians had also sunk some of their ships at the western end of the harbour. The allied navy could not, if this information proved to be true, send in ships against the defences on either side of the port. Any assault on the town would therefore have to be made from the southern, landward side and be carried out by infantry. He did add, and Captain Fortune translated, that the semicircle of defences on this side had been neglected. The enemy had always believed that any attack on Sevastopol would be made from the north. The Captain pulled out his little square sketch-map of the town. He said to his brother officers that, as an important naval port, it would surely be defended on all approaches. He then added some lines and arrows to the paper before putting it away.

While he had been talking, I found myself drifting away. I was back in Portsmouth and thinking of the hill above that town. Capture that hill, which had such a view of the harbour, and you can shell Portsmouth's docks to your heart's content and then take it. Perhaps with this intelligence that's what would happen to Sevastopol.

Captain Fortune's voice brought me sharply back to the present. While talking to the Tatars he had also been writing notes. He folded several small sheets of paper and with a crisp, "Take this to the commander-in-chief, at once," he handed them to a lieutenant of the 4th Light Dragoons.

Then off rode the cavalry, off lumbered the wagons and off we went to resume our patrol, but we were conscious of yet another troop of Cossacks that were keeping just out of range of our rifles. As the shadows lengthened, other wagons filled with fleeing Tatars passed through our lines. Not all of them though would escape the attention of the Russians; Cossacks, some of them in dark-blue tunics and trousers, others in a variety of other colours, with drawn sabres or lances and rifles slung across their backs, certainly pursued one group of wagons. Our focus though had to be on protecting the left flank of our army. But we remained very wary of their possible presence. We were, as we advanced over rocky ground, only too aware that what gave us good cover could also do the same for Russian snipers.

The day had been hot and from our vantage point, as we had looked back down earlier at the army spread across valley and hill, we could see helmets and greatcoats discarded by men who were close to exhaustion. Several soldiers even died later from their exertions.

We reached the River Bulganak, which was reduced to little more than a stream under the strong, late summer sunshine. We bivouacked, grateful for the rest. Those last few hours had been very hard going as we left the relative ease of the plain for the ridges and hollows of higher ground. The sun-baked river, barely allowed sufficient water for the men to fill their canteens.

There was now quite a lot of enemy activity and we caught glimpses of Russian cavalry or heard the clatter of horses' hooves on rocky ground.

***

A half-company of riflemen was sent to the top of a ridge as our cavalry, the 11th Hussars and the 13th Light Dragoons, returned from a probing patrol. The Royal Horse Artillery provided them with heavier covering fire as they made their way back. Cossacks had followed them in some strength, but shots from the rifleman persuaded them to go back beyond our range. One of the Hussars who rode past us had a shattered leg, but seemed to be rather unmoved by this involuntary amputation. The Cossacks still hovered nearby.

"Looks as though they are trying to draw us into an early fight," said a cavalry officer as he rode past our officers.

"It could also be an attempt to lure us into an ambush," offered Lieutenant Rennison of the Rifle Brigade.

Whatever the enemy's plan, it seemed that our army's commanders were just not ready to confront the Russians at this stage of the war and certainly not in the shallows of the River Bulganak. We knew from reports that had trickled down to us while we had waited at Kalamita Bay that a huge Russian force was collecting at another river, the Alma. The French, from the tall masts of their ships in the bay had seen lines of grey-coated enemy infantrymen digging trenches and building gunpits. It was also rumoured, but I never saw them, that the French Observation Corps were keen to use balloons to see more clearly what the enemy were doing. Captain Fortune had fallen into conversation with a French officer during our long wait on the beach and had been given that small map of the environs of Sevastopol.

***

If the Russians had been able to draw even a part of English and French forces into a skirmish at the Bulganak, or been able to catch them in ambush, then their large force at the River Alma would have an even greater chance of success.

Whatever they planned to do, it was obvious that the Russians were preparing to bar our way to Sevastopol. This would give them enough time to prepare their southern defences. If we failed at the Alma it would be our backs to the sea. Could we not send a force around the Russian lines at the river and then on to Sevastopol to lay siege to it or just storm in before all their defences were put in place?

Another obvious thing likely to help the Russians was the growing threat of cholera. Already, many men had been left behind at the bay where we had landed and more were joining the sick-list daily and not just cholera patients, but sufferers from a range of complaints. If was feared that if the heat of that day's march continued then many more men might also fall ill, so it was doubtful if there would be enough men fit enough to take on the enemy.

Riflemen too were suffering from the effects of the sun as it beat down on our dark green uniforms. As one of our jobs was to act in small groups as skirmishers, we carried quite a lot of kit to allow us freedom of independent action when and where needed. There was also something of a tradition for riflemen to live off the land; tactics learned in the American War, the Peninsula and, recently in the Cape.

As well as our rifle and sword in its scabbard, we often carried a knapsack with straps to carry a greatcoat, a mess tin, a plate in a canvas bag, a pouch containing sixty rounds of ammunition and percussion caps, a belt to hold the scabbard, a linen haversack and a water canteen. Quite often too we would also have a small cooking pot, blanket, spare socks, shirt and several days rations. The one piece of our uniform that did cause real annoyance and some inconvenience though, was the shako. It tilted forward, which gave it the feeling of wanting to fall forward. It made it difficult to move around especially when it was necessary to scramble over rocks and down gorges like those in the Crimea uplands. As a Company Sergeant, and there were usually six of us in each company, I did have the advantage, at least for a time, of a Kilmarnock bonnet instead of the ordinary rifleman's headgear. Later, most men found the issue of the bonnet or similar forage cap very welcome.

**

Early the next morning we were sent out to probe the Russian lines. Minutes later we topped a rise and looked across at the enemy's defensive positions on the other side, the south side of the River Alma. Under their commander, Prince Menschikov, the site was well chosen and looked quite formidable. The bank above, which was where his forces were stationed, rose quite steeply from the riverbank up to Telegraph Hill and then on down to the coast. To the east were the Kourgane Hills and looking very dangerous were two heavily fortified positions, the Great and Lesser Redoubts. These would not be taken easily. Our delay in leaving the bay had given them ample time to prepare their ground.

Facing the Russians on the seaward side, our right flank were the Turkish and French armies. At first we felt quite sorry for the Turks; their uniforms seemed ill-fitting and poorly made and their rations were meagre. This, our officers assured us, was down to their 'pashas' or military commanders, helping themselves to their stores first.

Straddling the road to Sevastopol were the English 3rd and 2nd Divisions with the 1st and Light Divisions on their left. My division, the 4th, was in the rear, held in reserve with cavalry on our left. Our immediate orders were to stop a squadron of Cossacks from attacking the left flank. This we managed to do.

If they ventured in range, we fired at them. After a while they pulled away. Leaving other companies to continue the vigil, sixty of us were permitted by Captain Fortune to move closer to Russian lines to try and keep Russian artillerymen's heads down, though this proved much easier said than done in the chaos of battle. The company's wag and prophet of doom exclaimed, "Why can't the buggers give us a chance and keep still instead of bobbing up and down?"

"Shall I nip over and ask my lord Raglan if he could send a message to the Russian commander to play fair?" replied his great pal, rifleman Dexter.

***

The attack began on Wednesday, 20th September with the ailing French commander St Arnaud sending men across the river. I couldn't understand why he had been put in charge of French forces in the first place. I had actually seen him land; he looked deathly pale and was obviously very ill, even then.

"Hope this is not a bad sign," observed Corporal Kingston as we looked across at the French advance and saw their leader slumped forward in his chair that had been placed on a hilly patch of ground overlooking the enemy, on the opposite side of the river.

As they advanced, naval guns from our ships opened fire in support. The French contribution to the attack was to scale the cliffs and try and draw the Russians from their hilltop defences. English soldiers would then cross the river and force their way up the hillside. Sir George Brown's Light Division and Sir George de Lacy Evans' 2nd Division began to move forward.

From about a mile away, Russian shells began to fall on the advancing men. Then the advance stopped. Lord Raglan must have decided to delay the push forward until the French had overrun their objective or had persuaded the enemy to send reinforcements from out of the two redoubts, and by doing so weaken their defences meeting the English attack.

The 1st Zouaves, in their distinctive blue tunics and red pantaloons, began to swim across the river and move up the hill using the rock-strewn slope as cover, much like a skirmishing rifle party would. Not only were they crossing the river, but they were also towing small artillery pieces across on makeshift rafts to the base of the cliffs. Then they began to haul not only themselves but these guns as well up the hill.

***

We were too far away to be really effective except to keep the Russians guessing, but we could clearly see, until gunsmoke ruined our view, shell and grapeshot landing on them at the top of the cliffs. The Russians though were maintaining heavy rifle fire from Telegraph Hill onto the advancing French forces. They were in desperate need of English soldiers to back them up before they were pushed down from the cliffs.

Captain Fortune shouted, "We need to get closer and give the Zouaves some coverin' fire. Our lads will get there too late to help."

He waved us forward with that steel half-bucket hilted sword, with the oak leaves and bugle decoration that I admired so much, grasped in his right hand while he held a Minié rifle in his left.

We moved forward, knelt but, almost as one man, we held back from firing. Even the best of shots might hit the Frenchmen now massing on top of the cliffs.

By around three in the afternoon, infantry from the Light, 1st and 2nd Divisions resumed their frontal assault. The Russians were still pouring deadly fire into them. As they moved forward, our 2nd Battalion moved in skirmish order to try and clear Russian sharpshooters from the orchards and vineyards beyond, who were firing into the advancing 30th and 50th Regiments. We in the 1st Battalion turned our attention once more to trying to keep the heads of the enemy gunners in the redoubts down, as the infantry tried to cross the river and move up the hillside.

We then noticed a force of Russian infantry advancing to the left of the 2nd Rifle Battalion, attempting to outflank them and so prevent them giving the advancing hill-climbers cover.

Lieutenant Axelby seeing this, rushed off with six riflemen of my company to fire at the trees above the 2nd Battalion to alert them of the danger posed by the Russians attempting to outflank them. The plan worked; several hundred men of the 2nd Battalion were ordered to form two lines and fire into the mass of Russians. Several hundred well-aimed shots prompted a swift enemy retreat.

Our infantry were now more than halfway across the river with rifles and pouches held high above their heads. Some we saw were swept away and doubtless drowned in the fast-flowing water. The river was deep and over time it had cut back deeply into the red soil, creating steep banks that added to the difficulty of climbing out. Further upstream there were shallows as the river broadened out, but these would not have given the army enough room to gather and then move up the hillside. Very soon the river was red with blood.

I also noticed that some officers were waving their drawn swords at their men. At first I had thought that they were just trying to encourage them forward, then I realised it was to threaten the infantrymen if they hesitated before stepping into the water.

"Poor bastards," one of the riflemen next to me muttered, "madmen waving swords behind 'em and madmen pouring shot into them!"

On the far bank, groups of men who had managed to cross the river seemed unsure what to do next. Several officers had fallen, including a major in the Grenadier Guards. He had had his head taken clean off his shoulders. His body had fallen forward and a stream of blood had gushed into the already crimson ribbon that was the River Alma.

The Russians above this melancholy scene looked ready to take advantage of the disorder below. We could see enemy officers urging their men to the edge of the hilltop from their earlier positions near the Great Redoubt, shooting as they advanced. As far as we could without hitting some of our own men who had managed to reach a point near the Russian defences, having been urged to even greater efforts by those surviving sword-waving officers, we opened fire. Fighting became a desperate hand-to-hand struggle. Shouts, screams, bugle-calls, shot and shell rolled across the field of battle as the deadly scene unfolded in front of us. My battalion, some distance from the grim main event, could do little but hope for success and be ready to move forward if called upon to add our considerable firepower to the melée.

The Russians needed to reinforce the ground around the redoubts as English infantry began to push forward after their hesitation. Then, as enemy infantry began to arrive in numbers they were fired on from their own guns on Kourgane Hill. Although shot falling on them caused some confusion, the Russians appeared to recover very quickly and with bayonets fixed began to charge our soldiers back down the hill.

***

Bodies littered the hillside, English red tunics alongside Russian grey.

In the confusion, the retreating soldiers of the Light Division met Scots Fusiliers charging up the hill. The picture though was a stirring one. To the left of the Fusiliers were kilted Highlanders, the 42nd, 78th, and the 93rd. Magnificent, exciting and confused before the Guards were able to re-group by forming two lines and pour concentrated rifle fire into the enemy. The Russions had no choice but to withdraw leaving many dead and wounded behind.

Scores of our own side began to push forward up the steep hill, but they were forced to step over the many bodies, both those barely alive and the dead, including many Highlanders.

The whole army was then ordered forward and we rejoined the rest of our battalion. We passed through shattered vineyards and orchards and caught up with a whole seething mass of bodies. Some were quite still while others writhed in pain. A lone enemy artillery piece began to fire in our general direction as we stumbled up the hill. One of our officers shouted a warning as a ball came bouncing down towards us. Our ranks parted as though we were carrying out a parade ground drill. It passed harmlessly between us and on down the hill. Several riflemen offended by this temporary halting of our progress took it upon themselves to fire on the Russian artillerymen responsible for the outrage. Only one man managed to scramble out of the gun pit and run for his life.

One of the injured Russians on the battlefield desperately indicated as we passed that he needed water. A spiked helmet lying by his side indicated that he was an officer of the 26th Infantry Regiment. One of my men sank to his knees, leaning his rifle against the left side of his body while he gave the wounded Russian his water canteen. The wounded man struggled to sit up. He raised the canteen to his lips, then dropped it! At the same time making a quick grab for a short sword half-hidden behind his back. As he attempted to run it through the rifleman, I rushed forward and, holding my rifle by the trigger-guard in my right hand and the barrel in my left, caught him in the chest with my sword. The triangular blade went in deep, forcing ribs apart as it sought a more vulnerable target. I twisted the rifle barrel and pulled it out. The Russian fell back gurgling blood, but was quite dead.

Harrison, who had nearly been skewered, gasped out a, "Thanks, sarge," then bent down and retrieved a very colourful icon from just inside the dead officer's tunic. "Might bring in a few pennies for this trophy," he added as he grabbed a silver cross set with gem stones and chain from the dead man's neck. He then continued up the hill.

All around other soldiers were relieving the dead and the dying of articles they no longer needed in this life.

We moved over to where some of our infantry had fallen to see if we could give them water or signal to the few stretcher-bearers and our own bandsmen to collect some of the injured. Some of their wounds were horrible, especially from injuries caused by cartridges and balls fired from the barrel of a rifle.

Russians bullets tended to be much heavier and longer than English and French ammunition. A hit from a round ball fired from a smooth bore musket was bad enough; it pushed a small piece of cloth or other uniform a soldier was wearing deep into the wound. This could, and very often did, lead if it was left unattended to infection, amputation and sometimes death. The wound from the long, cone-shaped bullet could also be very destructive, especially if it came into contact with bone.

Shots into soft parts of the body might make a neat, round hole going in, but it too could break bones as it smashed its way on through the body. Arms and legs were easily broken, sometimes leading to amputation. Stomach and lower intestinal wounds, as well as often ripping off a soldier's manhood and balls, were agonising and casualties might remain conscious and in pain for hours on end. Most wounds though caused some pain. Soldiers in South Africa caught by spear thrusts, rather than a bayonet inflicted wound, were no less painful and the dead were just as dead.

Bullets could also remove a man's face, leaving just a mangled mass without recognisable nose, mouth or teeth. That afternoon we had seen men with such injuries as these. Some men even staggered on with legs moving jerkily, until mercifully, shock and loss of blood or another hit to a vital organ put them out of their misery.

That evening, the battalion was ordered to bivouac on the hillside on the south bank of the River Alma, among the dead and the despairing cries of the wounded. This was a really miserable place to have to camp.

All night long cries of men in despair tore the night air.

**

The next day, the 21st September, the 4th Division began to move forward. In that early morning we found ourselves beginning our sombre task for the day and at the same position where the Russian right wing had faced the English 1st Division. We spent the day and most of the next burying the dead. This included a few men from our 2nd Battalion. Always a bit sobering to see a man wearing the same uniform laid out in death. We also delivered some of the wounded to field hospitals.

Not only were they suffering from a range of wounds, but they had to suffer with being bumped and jolted over rocks and rough ground as we carried them off in blankets. Stretchers were few and far between! One of them with wounds to the head, body and legs must have been suffering incredible pain and discomfort. I looked at his ashen, swollen face with his eyes rolling and his head lolling from side to side. We eventually reached the hospital and placed him on a table already sticky with blood.

"Sorry, boys," the surgeon said after a brief look at the man. "He's dead." He wiped his hands on his bloody apron.

The dead man we had carried in was then taken out by the two riflemen who had brought him to the table. Hardly had the body been removed before two field hospital attendants had replaced him with another man.

"Sergeant, hold this man down!" yelled the surgeon.

My lame efforts at protesting that I was urgently needed elsewhere were ignored. He came round the gore-covered table, pushed me unceremoniously to where the injured man's head was and said, "Hold him there," He indicated his upper arms.

The surgeon cut away the remnants of the man's 42nd Highlander's tunic sleeve, moving rather too closely to the fingers of my own left hand. Another tool was used to cut the skin and flesh from the bone. Making some effort to distract myself from the surgeon wielding the very sharp tools of his trade, my attention was drawn to the man's kilt. Sporran and kilt had been almost shredded by shell splinters. Little surprise that by this time the unfortunate man was in a dead faint.

"Ease off your weight on the left-hand side," he said, as he quickly raised a shattered remnant of arm. The bone in the upper arm was exposed just above the elbow. He then reached for a saw from a little table covered in bloody instruments. In about fifteen or so seconds, the useless limb was off and dropped into a bucket of what appeared to be red sawdust that reminded me of buckets I had often seen in a butcher's shop in Winchester. He swiftly tied off the stump, gathering up blood vessels and then seized a cloth from another bucket that had been left soaking in almost blood-free water and applied it to what remained of the man's limb.

Stretcher-bearers were then summoned and the man was carried from the tent. Seconds later another casualty was placed on the table. I made my excuses and hurriedly left. The wound itself had not unduly upset me, I was, unfortunately growing used to every kind of damage inflicted by all kinds of weapons with each passing day. What had been a shock though was the sound of the saw going through living bone. Scenes and sounds in the butcher's shop involved dead animals. This was different. These were men just like me.

I rushed back to where riflemen were still collecting the wounded only to be greeted by rifleman Dawkins.

"Thought you'd left us to become a surgeon's assistant, Sergeant Finch."

Of course he was joking, but unwittingly he had also put his finger on another of the problems we faced in this campaign. There was a shortage of people with medical knowledge. For most of the time that we had spent so far in the Crimea, our battalion of almost one thousand officers and men only had two surgeons – and at times just the one – two assistant surgeons and one hospital sergeant with any real idea of how to deal with wounds.

"No," I replied, "couldn't trust you to find your way to Sevastopol without me if I stayed here helping to saw off arms and legs."

Not long after this, one of the assistant surgeons died from cholera.

Conditions were not improving. Perhaps they were even worse as cholera victims were adding to the daily tally of the sick and those unfit for duty. We very soon lost another dozen men and a sergeant, as well as that assistant surgeon, to the disease.

Our lack of water and food and the difficulty in building suitable latrines on the rocky hillside was not helping. The River Alma served its purpose as a latrine but dead animals, dead soldiers and human waste was probably helping illness of one sort or another thrive. All around us was that sickly, sweet smell of death. Death that came in every shape and form. Men with stomach wounds looked at us with pleading eyes. Utter agony showed on their faces while their arms and legs were contorted as they writhed in a desperate but hopeless attempt to overcome their pain. Around us were men without stomachs, with lengths of intestine splayed all about. Flaps of skin and tattered bits of uniform were all that remained of previously healthy bodies and brightly coloured tunics and white and gold facings that would never grace another battlefield, let alone the parade ground where they belonged.

Several of the riflemen, very moved by this whole situation, looked at me, patting their rifles and glancing in the direction of some of these hopeless men.

"No, Williams, I know how you feel. I'm just the same. Best leave them to the surgeon," I said.

Williams, not given to showing much of anything, other than gloom, said, "I've shot a few dogs in my time. Couldn't let them suffer."

Sitting among all this death and despair could not help but reduce the morale of the men, yet there was a delay.

Perhaps the chaos of battle was the main reason why we were not hurrying off to lay siege or attack Sevastopol. Or perhaps the growing threat of cholera once again, or dehydration, or the drooping shoulders of a dispirited army as it began the trudge south was the reason. Whatever the cause there certainly seemed to be something hanging like that smell of death all around. The sky might be clear, but a cloud of gloom hung over the departing columns of men.

As we sergeants sat round our campfire on the evening of the 22nd September, the possibility that English and French commanders had absolutely no idea what action to take next was about to be aired. The whole situation, one of our number volunteered, was ridiculous. If our leaders didn't know what to do how were we expected to push the men on? It was also pointed out, as the rum flowed and the fire blazed, that it was not a very comforting thought either to remind ourselves that at the height of the battle of the River Alma a very confused commander-in-chief had been heard to call out, "Away you go, lads. Death to the French."

There were the French now our ally, dying all around in our common cause while our leader was fighting a forty-year-old battle.

The only small consolation was that if we were facing

difficulties then the Russians, who had been the ones to lose a battle and retreat in some panic after suffering thousands of casualties, must be in an even greater disorder.

Even more of a problem for the Russians, if the story that was now reaching us was true, was that as the enemy were pulling back they were too busy looting large estates abandoned by their owners who were fearful of what would happen after the defeat at the Alma. The Russians could therefore be falling into a disorganised rabble and should obviously not prove to be too much of a threat to us as we advanced.

The general view of we sergeants was that if our leaders acted immediately rather than hesitating then we would be successful aganst an enemy already defeated and suffering indiscipline Apparently the Cossacks had also run riot and had smashed everything in sight going from room to room in the big estate houses, or stealing anything they could carry away.

Tatar spies in the pay of our army told of the Russians utter disarray. The Tatars also seemed to be very pleased that the presence of the Turks, the same religion as themselves, would also greatly benefit them. All that was needed was the defeat of the Russians as soon as possible which, we learned, they felt should prove to be only just a matter of days away.

"Let's just press on now. Use the advantage we've got over the Russians and get it over with before they have a chance to call up reinforcements," was how Sergeant Richford summed up what we were all thinking. At least, whatever the plan, we had done our fair share after the battle on graveyard watch.

3

The army by the 23rd of September was toiling across the valleys of the Kacha and Balbec rivers. News was reaching us that many men were struggling as they moved through forests and the rugged terrain of the region. Although the days had been very warm, there was during the evening hours a noticeable chill in the air. Winter was not too far away and thoughts of being home by Christmas and the end of the year were evaporating.

At 7.00 a.m. on the 24th September, we had fallen in as usual but were then directed to some of the men of the 93rd who had fallen ill.

Cholera at this time also claimed the life of our battalion commander, Colonel Beckwith.

Drivers were commandeered and the sick men loaded on to wagons. Six riflemen and Sergeant Clements were assigned to escort them back to Kalamita Bay for the hospital in Scutari. Their escort was then to catch us up above Sevastopol as soon as possible. Our trail would be very easy to follow! After this delay we eventually struck camp above the Alma and began our progress down the road to that town with our usual tactic of pushing skirmishers ahead and above our flank. Around us a few houses and cottages still smouldered in the aftermath of the passage of Cossacks. The road though was more like the track around my village at home after heavy rain and the constant movement of carts, horses and wagons not improving one or the other.

We then moved off that rut-covered road that served as the main means of overland communication between the mainland and Sevastopol. We progressed through trees, mainly beech, though most had lost their upper branches as the Royal Horse Artillery had sent shells and grapeshot whistling through them in the general direction of Russian infantry. Our cavalry were also sent on ahead and chased the enemy, now fast retreating from the battle on the Alma. More horse artillery passed us and fired a few rounds into the Russians around a farm that lay a short distance from us. We noticed the French also hard at work harrying the enemy and after wrecking some of the farm buildings, moved on. Then we reached this Mckenzie's Farm. It had been called that after the name of the Scottish admiral who had lived there while designing and supervising the building of the naval arsenal in the town of Sevastopol, twenty years before.

"Trust a bloody Scotsman to give his name to this dump," said rifleman Wagstaff as we looked around for anything that might be useful. Wagstaff in the meantime had tipped a bucket of black, slimy sludge that days before might have been fresh, sparkling water, back over the edge of the broken well's parapet.

At least we had the chance to rest up, but, like Wagstaff, the rest of us were disappointed that those same French soldiers, who had passed this very same way such a short time before, had fired farm buildings and tipped rubbish down the wells. So our canteens remained empty.

All around the farm lay wagons abandoned by the Russians, including some that contained ammunition. We found out shortly after the reason for this. Lord Raglan had defeated a strong force of the enemy who had planned to seize English supply wagons, but instead were forced to abandon their own.

Having rested for a short time we resumed duties, carrying out orders to advance in skirmish line. We passed through orchards, the grass sticky from fallen apples as our boots skidded on their fermenting flesh. At last we reached a stream that provided us with water to fill our canteens with, which we had not been able to do back at the farm.

We also heard that our army had taken possession of a fort overlooking the port of Balaklava. This would at least give our fleet the chance to come and go with supplies, and, in spite of the distance from there to where we were likely to be stationed overlooking Sevastopol, it should result in our army being kept supplied. The French in the meantime had set up their headquarters at Kamiesh just south and west of Sevastopol. Of more interest was the news that the French from their position were able to see the southern shores of the Crimea. What concerned us all though was the fact that the Russians could be seen in and around the semicircle of defences that guarded the southern approaches to the town. They were frantically preparing their positions for a siege. They were not going to give up that easily. The initiative we had gained at the Alma was, like our hopes for an early return home, fast fading.

Our approach to Sevastopol had taken us south of the town and then we turned westwards on to high ground overlooking the port itself.

It had also given us a grandstand view of enemy activity and those fierce-looking defences that we would have to overcome if we were to take the town. There had seemed to be some hesitation on the part of English and French commanders in selecting the best places to begin the siege. It seemed to me that it would make sense for the French to occupy the left side of the uplands overlooking the town, as their supplies could easily come up from Kamiesh immediately to the south. If that was indeed so, then our securing Balaklava would give us the centre of the siege lines. Their superior numbers would almost certainly result in the French taking the ground to our right as well.

It also occurred to me as, along with most of the battalion, I looked down on the town, that if we were placed in the centre we would also be in quite an exposed position. If it had occurred to me then it would almost certainly have occurred to others including those who were likely to order us to attack those same defences.

Captain Fortune was also having misgivings in a conversation I overheard him having with a fellow company commander, Captain Marston-Brown.

"Looks as though we're going to be up against that bally great fort-like position there," he said, pointing at a formidable looking 'V'-shaped structure that seemed, even at this early stage, to be rather too close to us.

"It all rather depends on the old supplies," his fellow officer replied. "Let's hope this Balaklava is as good as they say it is."

"I'm not so sure," replied Captain Fortune, "a French officer I know drew me a little map and told me what Balaklava is like, or so he's been told. It's a bit small and too far to keep us regularly supplied. It's about an eight-hour haul for men and wagons over difficult ground. What about winter? We could still be here in January and February."

This view was something I had heard others talk about, let alone Mr. Fortune's French contact. Several artillerymen who had been present when the town had been taken said it was small, crowded and would give us problems. The town had also been taken with barely a shot being fired. The Russians seemed almost to have just handed it over. Did they know something we didn't? The Royal Artillery gunners had also said that Kamiesh, that the French now held, was everything that Balaklava wasn't!

That night we camped overlooking Sevastopol. As we were the nearest battalion to our final destination, my company was put on alert as the night picket. Though tired, we did expect an attack. Great efforts were made to keep everyone alert; it would, after all, make perfect sense for the Russians to try and catch us off guard before we had had time to properly dig ourselves in. They seemed, however, content just to fire perhaps fifty shells in our general direction. While we carried out our picket duty, the rest of the battalion had rations brought to them. Two hours later another company relieved us and we too managed to ease our hunger pangs as well.

***

During the early morning of the 27th after an earlier call to arms, we acted as a flanking guard but stopped short of Balaklava as supplies were brought up from the town for the whole army. As we moved around the camp helping to distribute forage for the horses and much-needed stores to the men, tents were being pitched in every direction. We then dropped back to our original position overlooking Sevastopol.

"Finch," said Lieutenant Axelby. "Captain Fortune wants you to stroll down to Balaklava and have a good look round. See what's what and report back to him."

So, travelling light, with just rifle, ammunition and water canteen, I told two riflemen, Hopton and Cosby, to come with me. We walked briskly down to the town. It looked as if a whole forest of trees had been used to supply the masts for the ships at anchor in the harbour there. Every size of vessel was jammed into the port. Around the quay were warehouses and low, tiled and thatched houses.

"Can we stop for half an hour, sarge?" asked Cosby, eyeing a very colourfully dressed youngish woman sitting outside of one of the thatched dwellings, drinking from a large cup. At intervals she blew him kisses and leaning forward offered her cup, as well as a fine view of two very well rounded breasts.

"No, he only needs two or three minutes," jeered his companion.

"Sorry to disappoint you, lads, but we've got to get back. No doubt you'll find your way back down here and over there again."

By this time we had walked the whole length of the harbour. Casks, boxes, lengths of timber, rope and supplies of every kind littered the quayside to the left and right of each gangplank. Commissariat officers were making desperate attempts to bring some order to the scene. Had the army been able to completely clear the town of people and the harbour of non-allied ships and take it over completely then the task of distributing supplies of food, fuel and ammunition would have been far easier than I feared it was going to be. We returned to camp and I reported to Captain Fortune.

"A shambles, then?" he said after I had relayed what I had seen.

***

At four the next day, officers roused us to parade quietly with only our rifles, swords and ammunition. We moved into position as directed, as a Russian regiment could be seen moving towards our lines. However, seeing our rifles levelled at them, they thought better of it and dropped back. From what prisoners had told English commanders they had learned a lesson at the Alma about how effective our Minié rifles were. Later though, heavy shelling rained down on our camp. We took no casualties but it was decided that we should pull back from our advanced, rather exposed position. Not that the one hundred yards or so reverse seemed enough, but at least we now had the benefit of rocky outcrops to shelter behind.

On the next day we were attacked by Cossacks. They had almost certainly been sent forward to test the strength of our defences. They looked a fearsome sight either with drawn sabres or their long lances approaching at the horizontal. They were also good at firing their long guns on the move.

We fired at them and achieved some success. One fell from his horse and rifleman Blake grabbed him and took him prisoner. He led the limping man towards Captain Fortune's position, jabbing him with his sword by way of encouragement.

As the two men passed Sergeant-Major Reeves, he said, "Well done, lad. I'll take him to Mr. Fortune. Extra rum for you."

Blake returned to his post, quite rightly looking very pleased with himself.

The Cossacks, minutes before this, had decided to withdraw and once again shells poured down on us.

It was decided that we move our camp again. This time we were just east of the Quarries. Our new position gave us a very good view of the town, although it also meant that we still remained a target for Russian guns. By now tents had arrived from Balaklava and although not much good against shells, we did have improved shelter from those increasingly chillier nights. Many riflemen tried to make their tents even snugger by cutting brushwood from the very few small trees that grew between the large rocks scattered all around our quarry defensive line. These quarries were only some three hundred yards away from that 'V'-shaped Great Redan and the obvious point from where an assault on the town would begin. This fact was also well known to the enemy who would make every effort to chase us out of our grandstand position.

In places, the front of the quarries rose, where trenches were dug, from about four to six feet on the inside.

This formed an excellent firing platform into the Russian lines directly ahead, the Great Redan and to the right of it an equally formidable position, Fort Malakoff.

Engineering officers and their working parties set to work on the 10th October, building artillery batteries. We acted as cover in case the Russians attempted a surprise attack to stop the gun-pits being completed.

All this was in preparation for the bombardment of Sevastopol that would be the first stage in the assault on the redoubts. The French had started to dig trenches and gun-pits the day before. Wearing steel helmets and metal chest protectors, dark trousers and carrying shovels and picks our French tunnelling allies reminded me of pictures I had seen of knights of old, dressed in armour ready to go into battle. It would also, like unhorsed knights, make it difficult for these metal moles to move very easily.

We provided more cover while lines for additional guns were laid, roughly parallel to Russian positions at what was called the Greenhill Battery. Just to the left and front of this position was what we referred to as caves. Captain Fortune said that there were two possible weak points in their defences, that in all other respects was fast sealing off the southern approaches to Sevastopol. One was roughly between the French left and our army's lines. There was a quarry that ran roughly south from where the town's inner harbour ended, down just near the ovens. On the other side of their half-circle of fortifications near the main harbour, Russian forces could get out and move down towards the Inkerman Heights.

**

First of all the left half of our battalion after parade was sent to occupy the trenches in support of the working parties. The next day, the right half took over the duties, but as they did so the enemy chose that moment to pour down heavy fire on them.

During this first week or so of October, some of our sick who had been shipped to the hospital at Scutari returned to our ranks. They told stories of poor conditions. Men had been set down on decks that were awash with seawater as ships pitched and rolled. Men had cried out in pain but received little or no attention. The wounded that died were then just thrown overboard. The survivors, on being carted to the hospital, found conditions there no better.

Wards often had no beds, but mattresses made of little more than a straw-filled sewn sheet, often stained with the blood of the previous occupant, covered the filthy floors. The wounded were everywhere; in beds, in between beds and in the corridors. The dead, among those still hanging on to life. There were shortages of everything from bandages to medical attention. Everywhere, they told us, was the foetid smell of death. Bloodstained dressings, human excrement and urine mingled with the cries of the injured. The few medical staff that was available just could not cope.

On the 13th October, while our left wing was on duty, the rain poured down as we lay in our trenches. Large numbers of shells from both sides were continuously passing over our heads during this and many other days and nights.

***

We almost got used to the whine of shells, the clatter of varying sizes of grapeshot on rock, the shriek, as the odd piece of splintered rock or metal hit a man. There also seemed to be an ever-present pall of smoke from the town to our lines. We also became the sole target, or so it seemed, for a large mortar battery to send its huge fizzing bombs rather too close to our camp for comfort. So Lieutenant Axelby and I took a party of sixty riflemen out in an effort to silence it. We concealed ourselves about 200 or so yards from the Great Redan, where the offending battery was situated and waited for daylight. We were successful in not only killing the mortar crew but seven or eight other artillerymen as they peered over the parapet to see where the firing was coming from. One of our successful methods was to work in pairs. The better shot of the two would do the shooting, the other would spot the target and give exact details as to where to aim. Some of the spotters used a telescope, which made the task much easier. We spent most of that day just firing into the Redan at anything that moved.

A couple of days later while we in the battalion's left wing took our turn in the trenches, the Russians shelled the whole length of the English lines in concentrated artillery fire. We were lucky to escape serious injury. Just a few small wounds caused by small stones thrown up as shells exploded on the quarry rocks.

From our trench, later that same day we mounted several reconnaissance missions nearer to the Redan to see just what damage had been inflicted on it and how many guns they had used when they had raked our positions on the 15th October.

***

There was some damage. Parts of the abbatis, where felled trees with sharpened ends faced the likely direction from where the Russians would expect an attack to come from, had been largely destroyed. Yet, most of the length of the enemy's defences beyond the abbatis was being hastily restored to its earlier condition. We met a small force of French infantry engaged in a similar task though their attention, not unnaturally, was mainly concerned with the Malakoff. There were also sorties by men of other regiments as well as artillery and the engineers. As for guns, we counted well over one hundred in the Russian batteries. There were certainly likely to be others and many covering the sides of the redoubt against any broad assault by our infantry. The Great Redan, as we could see it, was like a huge 'V' with the point of the 'V' facing us.

As we returned to our own lines we took special care as, with so many men out on probing sorties of one kind or another, we might be taken for a force of Russians trying to do the same to us. There had been a score or more attempts already to infiltrate French lines, officers had told us, and those on duty in the trenches were told to keep especially on the alert.

Behind us were explosions, smoke and fire, and that added to the problem of returning safely. As we were going back we provided perfect targets to both sides. We were silhouetted against the Russian defences behind and the rising ground to English lines in front of us.

We were told when we eventually got back that our artillery was now in position and several hundred guns would soon open fire.

The English and French fleets would also be bombarding the forts on, or overlooking Sevastopol harbour.

At 6.30 a.m. on the 17th October, the first of their concentrated bombardments on the town began from our lines. Artillery that included two huge 68-pounders, which delivered massive blows on the Great Redan.

The Russians somehow managed to retaliate and minutes later one of their shells landed on a French gun emplacement on Mount Rudolph. Lieutenant Axelby and I were once again told to take a party of riflemen to try and keep the heads of the enemy gunners down. We had also been ordered to take trenching tools with us to make depressions to lie in. Not an easy task to achieve on hard, stony ground and with the certainty of enemy rifle fire or worse, falling on us.

"We're digging our own bloody graves," grumbled Williams as tools hit hard rock. Pickets in the Russian lines must have heard and had probably seen us in between the whine of shells overhead. I had seen enough men losing everything below belt-level from shell and grapeshot to encourage me to grind my groin as close to the ground as possible as we lay face down. It did give the manhood some protection and at last being able to drop into any trench no matter how shallow was some comfort. Then, as we were able to fire independently and were used to loading and shooting in the most uncomfortable of settings, we were able to inflict some damage on the enemy.

Williams, though an excellent shot, was always the one man in the company who could easily find doom and gloom in any situation.

The situation could have been made for him as he muttered his own commentary on our situation. "Russian death coming our way," he announced as a shell hissed over our heads.

"It came from over there. Next time that bastard artillery officer bobs up again I'll bag him," he said, and a second later he fired and the bobbing bastard officer, bobbed his last!

Williams then started singing, but that proved too much for the lieutenant, "Shut up, Williams. Just concentrate on the enemy."

The voice reduced to barely audible obscenities, which I could only hear because I was less than a rifle's length from our very own Crimean songbird. He still managed though to shoot a good number of Russian artillerymen from his grave. Shots also rained down on us and there was a great feeling of relief as darkness fell and a bugle recalled us to our camp. Only two of our number had sustained any wounds and these, once again were not too serious. Luck was still with us.

That explosion on Mount Rudolph had caused serious damage, including the detonation of an ammunition store. It certainly seemed to have confused them. Sergeant Clements told me as we drank rum that evening that he had seen them just wandering around looking very dispirited. Not like the French we were used to seeing swaggering about their camp.

Our artillery had also had some success finding and destroying a gun battery on the Malakoff Redoubt.

This was good but still left something like another forty-nine to overcome. This fort was opposite French lines and they would have to launch themselves against it. Like the French, the enemy seemed to be rushing around in some confusion and we wondered why the order to attack had not been given.

"Well, that's it again, Jack," said Sergeant Clements, "we're not pushing forward to build on success. Johnny Russ will have rebuilt it all again by tomorrow and we'll have to do it all over. What's the bloody point of shelling them if we give 'em a chance to recover?"

A reason for the hesitation and the decision not to attack at once gradually emerged later. The damage to their Mount

Rudolph battery had certainly caught them off guard; morale had suddenly dropped and they just weren't ready to support any attack we could have made. Again, unusual for the French as they were generally ahead of us in wanting to attack first and worry about it later.

What had been obvious from our very advanced position earlier in the day was that both forts, the Great Redan and the Malakoff, were going to be almost impossible to take unless severe damage was done to them before our attack, and we moved before the Russians had time to recover and make more repairs. This thought must play on the minds of any force leading an attack! The Redan, our likely target, had a ditch immediately in front of its very steep almost sheer walls. In front of the ditch was the abbatis. We surely would have fared better had we attacked immediately after the Alma. The Russians had managed very successfully to reinforce their whole southern line, protecting the town.

It occurred to me that if they were capable of doing that after a defeat, what else were they capable of doing?

4

During the early evening of the 21st October, I was ordered to report to our battalion commanding officer's quarters. Unlike our rather meagre, bell-shaped tents, this particular lodging had been constructed with a drainage ditch around its whole perimeter. Just inside of this was a small stone wall tracking around the ditch. Canvas, held up by a central pole, fanned out to the edges, which were held down by a layer of stones. Worth copying, I thought, if I could lay hands on some materials.

I heard muffled voices as I approached the back of the colonel's tent. I hesitated, but could barely help eavesdropping. Even sergeants don't get told everything so I strained to hear more.

The words, "… cipher had been destroyed in St Petersburg, but we strongly suspect that one of the ambassador's documents had been removed beforehand, possibly by one of their spies," floated towards me.

As I stood there, another voice broke in, "We just don't know how much information the Russians have about our lack of preparedness for this campaign. Our failure to follow up the success at the Alma may cost us the war. All they may be thinking is 'just hold out long enough', wait for our morale to drop even further and then come out and just mop-up the dregs of our armies. Look what happened to the French after Rudolph."

The first voice I had heard broke in, "It would greatly help our cause if we knew what they are planning to do."

"That," said another voice, "is why, gentlemen, you have been summoned here."

At that moment, a burly rifleman brought the point of his sword to within an inch of my nose, while a second picket came towards me from the other side of the tent and stood behind me.

"Who goes there, sarge?" the first one asked.

I told them that they knew only too bloody well who I was, but I did add that I was impressed they were alert enough to issue a challenge. They motioned me forward. At the tent entrance they called out, "Sergeant Finch reporting as ordered."

A tent flap opened and an arm beckoned me inside.

The interior was thick with cigar smoke. I moved towards a table strewn with maps. At the end of the table, leaning his elbows comfortably on an 'Army and Navy Stores' hamper was my battalion commander. I stood to attention, saluted and waited.

My company commander, Captain Fortune, told me to stand at my ease and then proceeded to introduce me to the assembled officers.

"This is Sergeant Finch," he said.

At this point I recognised among the mainly moustachioed faces staring intently at me the very familiar face of General Cathcart, the commander of the 4th Division.

He had made his headquarters on top of a hill, commanding an excellent view of the whole of his division and a grander one of Sevastopol. Very soon this would become widely known as Cathcart's Hill. A few of us had felt that, had he been in overall charge of the army, then we would already be sitting in the town. Many, and not just those who had served under him in South Africa, regarded him as a fine, very quick-thinking officer and one not likely to sit around hesitating, unlike some field officers we could mention.

Slapping me on the back, he declared enthusiastically, "Any member of the Rifle Brigade is to be relied on. This man is no exception. He is sober, reliable and an excellent shot."

"That'll make a change after the drunkenness and floggings at

Varna then," added another officer rather sourly, but accurately!

"Well, Finch," began the colonel, "we have rather a special job that needs doing. I take it that I have your assurance that anything you may have heard," jerking his thumb towards the back of the tent, "or will hear or see in this billet, goes no further."

I mumbled, as I looked across at my company commander that they could rely on me.

He continued, "Mr. Fortune recommended you be part of a sortie into town. This officer," indicating one of the officers who had not yet spoken, "needs to get into Sevastopol to collect what may prove to be vital information. The plan is for a small party to go in behind another group of riflemen, led by this officer here, Colonel Windham," indicating an officer dressed in the uniform of a quartermaster-general, attached to the 4th Division. I noticed that, as he leaned against the table smoking a pipe, he shifted his weight awkwardly from one leg to another. Captain Fortune later told me that this was the result of a kick from a horse.

Fortune, with a nod of the head from the colonel took up the briefing.

"There will be Major Rivers here, me, yourself and two riflemen. You will select two men. Any suggestions who?" he asked.

"Yes, sir. I would go for Abel and Williams. Both very good shots, experienced when it gets down to the hand-to-hand stuff, and both good at moving silently."

Captain Fortune added, "Yes, good enough, but tell them nothin'. Once we get into the town we shall move towards the old part of Sevastopol. What they don't know won't hurt them and it'll save Williams moanin' about it."

As he was speaking he was smoothing out one of the maps.

"We are here," he said, stabbing at a point on the still crumpled sheet with his cigar. "Colonel Windham's party of a sergeant and six riflemen will leave just ahead of us at 3.00 a.m.

and make their way down to the trenches. They will be followin'
a company of the 21st Regiment to a ruined house on the left side
of the ravine. There will be engineers and a workin' party nearby
buildin' a battery. To our right, the French will be engaged in
doin' the same. We hope the Russians will be too occupied
coverin' all this activity to notice us as we slip off to the left of
the Great Redan here." Another stabbing of the map. "Then we
slip over their lines and enter the old town between the Barrack
and Garden Batteries. From our observations, their defences
are only thinly manned at this point. Once inside, we head for
the Kutusov Boulevard and a particular house. You are bein'
told this because your main task is to protect this officer," he
indicated Major Rivers, "and make sure he reaches that house."

He then added with some amusement, "And returns."

The battalion commander took over the briefing,

"As Captain Fortune has already said, it is not usual for such
details to be shared with anyone other than officers, but I know
– we all know – that you can be trusted with such a dangerous
and important mission."

I felt myself wincing at the word 'dangerous' but hoped that
it hadn't shown on my face.

Fortunately, my company commander continued,
"Obviously, this is no easy task. We shall be passin' near some
heavily defended Russian positions and then deep into enemy
territory. Once inside Sevastopol there will be no friendly faces.
With a little luck we shall reach our house by first light, conduct
our business and be back by late tomorrow night. We hope that
a few more grey uniforms," waving at some captured Russian
tunics and greatcoats as he said it, "will go unnoticed."

The look on my face, somewhere between amazement at the
huge scale of the job to be done, incredulity and embarrassment
at the praise I had received and their apparent trust in my ability,
prompted General Cathcart to ask if I had any questions.

I had, tinged with my overall feeling and a little concern

that encouraged me to be rather more inquisitive than I would normally be. It was usually a good idea in the army not to ask too many questions and my sergeant's rank also meant that I took orders and made sure that others carried them out without asking the reasons why.

"Yes, sir. What will we find in that house?"

"You shall find a Tatar. I understand you have already met up with them. It's no secret they have no fondness for the Russians. Over the last fifty years or so they have been very badly treated by the Tsar. We are reliably informed that one of the Tatar spies our government employs, has obtained some information that indicates how the Russians intend to act when Sevastopol falls."

The general continued, "You saw how things were when we landed and how after the Alma we just did not press ahead and secure the town. We need to know if they plan to reinforce the Crimean Peninsula or abandon it and try and bottle us up here."

I could not nor would not dare, if I valued my sergeant's rank, in such honourable company dispute the present situation or be too quick to agree to what was, or so it seemed to me the fault of our leaders why we were outside rather than inside the town.

General Cathcart's tone of voice did rather suggest that it would have been a different matter had he been in total command of the whole of our force. This only confirming my earlier thoughts and those shared by my fellow sergeants in the company. Even to ordinary soldiers it had been a missed opportunity. This hesitancy on the part of the leadership would likely to be the cause of many casualties among those same men in the fighting yet to come.

Our army, that looked splendid on the parade ground, that had battled in the main very courageously at the River Alma, felt let down and demoralised.

"Well, if there is nothin' more," said Captain Fortune, "we

should go and prepare. Back here then, Finch, in two hours' time."

I was just about to ask what equipment we should take when he added, "You and your two men are to bring rifles, swords, ammunition, water canteens and two days food supplies. Tell them to leave their shakos behind – a bit too cumbersome for creepin' about rocks, houses and rubble. Might give the game away if on top of your Russki tunic and greatcoat you've got an Albert shako on your head. They can have one of these forage caps. They look near enough like the Russian types."

***

I returned to my corner of the camp feeling dazed, if not overwhelmed, by the events of the previous hour or so. I reflected that, for all their faith in me, I might have been better off not knowing any of the details – less to worry about certainly. I found Abel and Williams and just told them they were wanted for an extra duty. I informed them of what to bring and said they were to be at headquarters in ninety minutes time.

Williams, in his usual way, wandered back to his tent mumbling darkly about the parentage of officers and sergeants. I did catch, "… daft bastards," as he disappeared into the gloomy interior of his shared billet to collect his equipment. I felt he wasn't too far from the truth in his mutterings and that was even before he had any idea of our mission and its dangers!

We assembled as directed and spent a few moments kitting ourselves out in the captured Russian uniforms. I noticed that both officers carried revolvers and Mr. Fortune also had a rifle. He was, after all, as good a shot as most riflemen with the *Minié*. Officers in most regiments tended to be disliked; they were after all a very privileged class. Whatever others felt about the officer class, he was generally respected. He put himself at risk alongside his men. He also, like most of the officers in the Rifle Brigade, liked to keep his men informed, where appropriate, of events and what was expected of us. For some reason though, I always seemed among the very first in the company to be told about future actions. Too many officers in the army just gave the orders.

It might have been a good idea though if we had been given revolvers as well. The rifle was perfect for long shots, but could be cumbersome in close fighting. We could still have taken the rifle to merge in with enemy infantrymen, but a revolver might come in handy if we found ourselves too close to the Russians. Still, we had the sword if it got to hand-to-hand encounters or if we had to move quickly over rocks or through houses. But rifle and sword when fixed, measured well over the length of the men who carried it. And as most officers bought their own revolvers, perhaps issuing us with our own might have been one step too far, even for Captain Fortune.

Colonel Windham's party of a sergeant, that very same man who I had almost bowled over at Westminster some four years before, and the six riflemen moved off, following the men of the 21ˢᵗ towards the trenches. Colonel Windham moved with a distinct limp following that encounter with a horse. Then the party moved on past the half-completed battery and the ruined house. Soon, we all came across a French working party carrying material to build a battery that would be directly opposite the 'V' of the Malakoff. This bastion was, like the Redan, going to be a formidable challenge. As Colonel Windham's party broke right, we filed left. From then on we were on our own.

In the eerie light of the early morning, a mixture of fog and smoke hung over Sevastopol. We could though still see the town and harbour in front of us. *Let's hope they can't see us too clearly*, I thought, as I pulled the Russian greatcoat around me and held my rifle in readiness.

The early morning mist and the almost continual pall of smoke that seemed to clothe the town added a smoky storey to the ruined houses and defensive positions.

We had passed very carefully by the Barrack Battery. Then picked our way over heaps of rubble. Broken glass, doors and window frames lay smouldering. A strong smell of smoke irritated the nostrils. Suddenly a shot rang out. Instantly and instinctively we flung ourselves to the ground. A running figure shot past me and then crumpled in a heap about twenty yards behind me. Seconds later a small party of Russian infantry passed by. They kicked the fallen figure, laughed, but then moved on. They should have seen us but were too busy gloating over the fate of their quarry. He may have been a spy, a deserter or a looter.

Captain Fortune tapped me on the shoulder and we all moved off but with that queasy feeling in the pit of the stomach expecting at any moment a Russian musket ball to smack into me.

After fifteen minutes of sweaty, fearful progress, we stopped. Major Rivers signalled for us to climb through what had once been a window. In front of us, as dawn light picked its way through the smoke-laden gloom, we saw a room littered with broken furniture. A piano with the remains of a fallen chandelier across the keyboard lurched at an angle on two damaged legs. This had once been a very grand room of a very grand house. Fallen plaster and smashed timber roof trusses, broken mirrors and ornaments covered the floor. The roof had gone; it looked as though a shell had hit it and brought down the ceilings and the floors of the rooms below them.

Our boots scraped across the rubble, but any noise we were making was being drowned out by the singing and carousing from next door. Candles, lantern light and the rays of the rising sun were casting odd shadows across the plasterless walls as we looked to find a place to hide and rest up. We moved towards the back of the house, trying not to sneeze in the dust-laden atmosphere. Williams and Abel led the way as they headed towards the right-hand corner of the room. A large crack where bricks had been blown out caught their attention. Abel bent low and moved towards it and from where we were standing, a mellow, orangy-yellow glow could be seen coming from the house next door. Abel's movement s disturbed yet more plaster-dust, which floated in the light from the gap in the wall and gave the whole corner, a snow-like appearance.

He motioned Williams to join him and within a few seconds both men were desperately trying to stifle their sniggering.

"Will you just look at those titties!" exclaimed Abel.

I joined them at the gap in the wall hissing to them to hold their noise. In front of us lay a large room illuminated by many candles. Any daylight that might have been lucky enough to creep in was kept out by curtains over where doors had once been, giving passage to the front of the house.

Down the left-hand half of this room were a number of curtained-off areas. The first had another ill-fitting curtain opposite where the wall should have been and where we were then looking across. At right angles to the curtain was another length of similar material suspended from an exposed ceiling timber to form a makeshift door. The back wall opposite this piece of cloth seemed to have survived shot and shell from our gun batteries, and as far as we could tell was almost intact down the whole length of the house. These box-shapes were repeated and probably occupied the length of this side of the room but were out of our immediate field of view. From our vantagepoint we managed to catch more than a glimpse of a large, sweating Russian, easing himself up from the horizontal postion while attempting to button his trousers. On the cot-bed lay a woman, naked from the waist up and with a bosom as imposing as the Great Redan and the Malakoff. Her under-skirts were pulled to one side. Throwing a few coins into a brass-looking jug, which we could just see was on a small table, the Russian infantryman, for that was what his uniform showed he was, put on his tunic, took a long drink from a bottle, pulled the curtain door to one side and staggered out. Pausing for a few comments and a few gestures to a file of three or four men, he lurched out and on into the rising, morning sun. The men remaining, of which one's meat member was at attention as though on parade and in anticipation of their turn to storm the female bastions waiting in the curtained-off enclosures, looked enviously at the just-pleasured Johnny Russ as he passed them. From elsewhere in the house came noisy, drunken voices singing lustily if not tunefully.

I, too, was feeling some stirrings from seeing the delights of the whore house. What the three of us hadn't quite been able to see we were busy imagining and conjuring up from memory. It had after all been some time since I had experienced such active service. The scene before us took me back to that time I had been tempted while the battalion waited for sailing orders back in Portsmouth. Just beyond the dockyard walls, in I think Queen Street, Portsea, were similar establishments where anything could be bought and all tastes taken into account. However, a chance encounter with a blue jacket in a local beer house opposite the dockyard's main gates changed my intentions.

As we drank to each other's health and to the risks to us that the forthcoming war was likely to offer, he said, "You can get anything you want there," jerking his thumb in the direction of the road I had planned to walk down. "And," he added, with a meaningful glance at my trousers, "anything you certainly wouldn't want!"

He then went on, "I have heard it said that few streets anywhere at night are worse than that street."

That rather ended our conversation and my enthusiasm. So I returned to barracks, pennies and a lot else besides, safe.

In some ways I was very relieved when a whispering voice brought me back sharply to the Crimea.

"Finchy, we're in the wrong bally house."

At that, Captain Fortune motioned us out of the corner of the room.

**

We clambered out of the house and took a right turn behind the building offering Russian delights and moved on. As all houses showed roughly the same level of damage, I suppose the mistake was an easy one to make. We, in due course, arrived at the rear of another building, hopefully the correct one. Williams pushed aside a splintered door that squealed in protest at being disturbed, its hinges no longer really carrying out their original function. Still, noises from that drunken revelry were managing to pierce the morning air. Had they gone on all night, or had it been a very early start?

Once inside what we all hoped was our correct destination, we began to carefully feel our way around the walls. The interior was gloomy, but we managed to find a kitchen. Littering the floor were pots, pans and scraps of food. Then from the depths a voice called, "Etes-vous anglais?"

Behind the voice in a very heavily bearded face, gleamed some very white teeth with a noticeable gap between the top two front ones.

Major Rivers moved forward, ushering the stranger into a corner and then, after an exchange in French, returned to where we stood. The officer told us there was a cellar leading off from the kitchen. It would be dry and safe down there and with proper care we could light candles rather than just sit in the dark. I also thought that if somehow our presence was discovered that we would be caught like rats in a trap. Williams was ordered to remain at the top of the cellar steps on watch.

Once down the cellar, the bearded man moved the slide from the lantern he had been holding and by doing so threw his quite substantial shadow on the wall behind him. He was tall, well-

built, with twinkling eyes that seemed never to be still. Perhaps
in his line of work he couldn't afford to rest his gaze in only
one direction. He did look like so many of the Russians we had
caught in our sights. I learned later that he had been a merchant
like his father and grandfather before him in Balaklava, trading
in goods from across the Black Sea and into the Mediterranean.
He was a Tatar and had married a Russian, but generally had
no love at all for them. His family had been thrown off their
lands and replaced with Russians. Now the allies were besieging
Sevastopol and he was going to do all he could to pay them back.
With his looks, a Russian wife and links to trade, he was useful to
the many Russians who still relied on him for their own wealth
through trade and supplying the Army and Navy. He was so
far still able to move around Sevastopol and beyond with some
freedom. He had, to protect himself, appeared to have made a
show of being a follower of the Russian Orthodox Church rather
than his own Moslem tradition; a move which, I was told, would
not be very acceptable to other Moslems.

I did wonder, even with the freedom he had, how he would
have laid hands on information that might be useful to us.
Perhaps money is the key to that particular door. Anyway, there
was a pouch from one of his pockets with maps and other papers
now in Major Rivers' hands.

**

Mr. Rivers, barely able to control the excitement he was
obviously feeling, repeated in English for the benefit of the rest
of us much of what the Tatar had told him and we were close
enough, confined as we were in the cellar, to overhear. It also,
while they talked, gave two of us, while the third remained on
guard, a chance to rest and eat some breakfast of bread, meat
and water.

He then added, "He's given us a map showing where the

Russians have reinforced or plan to reinforce their redoubts. More worryingly, if we go for a frontal assault on the Redan and Malakoff, the likely places where they will lay mines. It also indicates when they might do this work and how they intend on forcing us to the north of the Crimean Peninsula and catch us napping at Evpatoria. We need to get back with this stuff as the Russians look about ready to take back Balaklava in the next few days."

We moved to the top of the cellar. The morning light outside was far too bright for us to risk moving off. We would have to wait until after dark.

Further conversation followed between Major Rivers and the Tatar.

"He seems to think," he said, "that we should be safe enough in the cellar until just before sunset. Provided we don't move about too much, or the place attracts the attention of passing soldiers, our routine shelling of the town should keep them occupied and away from here. Then, if they follow their usual routine, there will be a guard change and the rebuilding of the daily damage to their defences. Hundreds of Russians will be just milling around and with luck we can merge in with them."

Captain Fortune added, "We've got food, water and shelter and if we divide the rest of the day into two-hour guard duty shifts it should go quite quickly. Apart from anythin' else, I don't think we have much choice."

With that he pulled out his double hunter watch, something else I greatly admired, placed it on a little shelf and said, "It's 10:17 now. I'll do the first two hours, Abel the next, then Williams and you do about 4:15 to 6:15 p.m, Finchy. By then it'll be dark and we'll be able to slip away."

The rest of us crunched on biscuits, cheese and dried meat, washed down with water and settled down to doze as only soldiers can: asleep instantly, alert at once. An old leather bucket covered with a piece of cloth served as our latrine. Not surprisingly we would be leaving that behind us when we quitted the cellar. Something else occurred to me at this time: officers and men may occupy very different stations in life, but in performing some duties we were all very similar.

Shellfire interrupted my thoughts and occasionally the ground beneath us shook, walls seemed to move and plaster showered us. Not too far away we could, when taking our turn on guard, hear Russian voices, the squeak of wagon wheels and the clatter of hooves as horses made unsteady progress across rubble-strewn streets. Neighing sounds adding to my belief that they were really struggling with heavy caisson and artillery pieces.

At long last Major Rivers looked at his watch, glanced at Captain Fortune and said, "I think it's time to go. Remember all of you that, if I am hit, you must get these papers back at all costs. You may have heard earlier that it is very likely that the Russians plan a counter-attack to drive us from the heights. This attack could be as early as the 25th. Today is the 22nd so we must get back in the next few hours."

We left our hideout after a quick look round to make sure that nothing was left behind that might give away the fact that Englishmen had been there. The bucket was carefully buried under some rubble. Slowly we retraced the route that we had followed into the town. This, before that large house with its sundry entertainments was once again a hive of happy activity. After a few minutes walking I noticed that the Tatar seemed somehow to have just melted away. Soon we were closing on the Garden Battery. Although it was hours after sunset and should have been as black as pitch, the light from many still burning fires – a result of our shelling – was illuminating rather too well our way near the usually thinly-manned enemy defensive line. Then a voice challenged us. I raised my rifle and shot the grey uniform barring our way. I hoped that with all the noise around us my shot would merge with it and go unheeded, but three more Russians appeared. They looked startled at first as they tried to make sense of our motley uniforms.

"Rush them, lads," yelled Captain Fortune.

I moved quickly forward with Williams and Abel on either side of me. We took them just as they were deciding just who we were.

My companions shot two of them while I, not having time to reload, caught the third one in the throat with my sword.

We ran quickly to the defensive trench, climbed the parapet to the left of the battery and dashed as quickly as we could in the direction of our own trenches. Just as we prepared to drop down to the relative safety of these advanced positions, several shots hissed past us. There was a groan and Abel fell. With Captain Fortune, rifle in hand, covering me, I bent over the still form of Abel.

"Go on," shouted Fortune to the others as I searched Abel's back for the wound. I eased my forefinger across a round hole now oozing blood in the borrowed greatcoat and underneath his own rifle-green tunic. The bullet had shattered his spine.

"Nothing we can do for him, sir," I said, as I picked up Abel's rifle as well as mine. I crouched low and followed Captain Fortune in pursuit of Major Rivers and Williams.

Less than an hour later we were all standing in the battalion commander's quarters.

"You have performed your duty well," he said, as Williams and I were thanked and dismissed. As we left he turned to the two officers heaping praise and congratulation on them for a mission carried out successfully. The documents would soon be on their way to the commander-in-chief by special messenger.

***

We returned to our part of camp with Williams complaining as usual about officers, the lot of the private soldier and the injustice of it all.

"Poor bastard, Abel. From a hovel in London to a bullet in the back in this shit-hole. Another fifty yards or so and he would have been all right. And, sarge, if there are any medals going for what we've been through, two guesses who won't get them."

With that, he said nothing more just entered into a sullen mood and fixed a gloomy stare on the ground in front of us as we walked back.

5

I wondered what would happen next. Had we really achieved anything by our sortie into Sevastopol? After all, after their defeat at the Alma, a bit of shelling and the occasional probing of our lines, the Russians had been fairly quiet. Were they reserving their strength for an attack as the Tatar's documents indicated, and did they have sufficient forces to do so? Would our leaders actually do anything with the information we had brought from the town and which one of our number had died for? After all, hesitancy seemed to be what some of them had proved themselves to be good at. *We shall see*, I thought.

On our side of the siege lines there had been activity in recent days. General Cathcart could look with satisfaction from his headquarters on his hill all the way down towards Inkerman at the orderly rows of tents. Around Kadokoi, the Royal Horse Artillery had established their camp. In almost every direction, the impression was of our growing strength. Would the Russians be brave or reckless enough to take all this on with a counter-attack? Their defensive line extended from the western end of Sevastopol Harbour and continued across the Charnaya River and not too far short of Mckenzie's Farm. So it was not impossible that they might try something.

To protect our supply lines coming up from Balaklava along the Vorontsov Road, the Turks had busied themselves building and manning six redoubts. The first of these was situated on what became known as Canrobert's Hill.

Another was on the southeastern edge of the Causeway

Heights. Two more overlooked the North Valley and the final two were at the western edge of the South Valley.

We were told by Captain Dugdale of the Highlanders during a tour of our defences that the Russians appeared to be watching our left flank to the north of Balaklava. I was detailed with thirty men to accompany Dugdale as he rode around the Heights. Tents, horses, ammunition, boxes, artillery caissons and men engaged in various activities stretched out in every direction.

I also caught sight of the Light Brigade under Lord Cardigan waiting at the western end of the North Valley. General Scarlett's Heavy Brigade had moved to cover the South Valley should the Russians try and attack the allies from the northeast. It looked as though the information we had brought back might have been put to some good use after all. I had that uneasy feeling that something was about to happen.

Captain Dugdale returned to where the 93rd Highlanders were encamped. They were on a slight rise where they could clearly see any Russian movement across the Causeway Heights.

If the Russians did attack from the northeast then the Turks could be in for a very bad time along those Heights.

As was fast becoming the custom, a company of riflemen was sent out with orders to 'harry' any Russian advance. Through the morning mist we could just see the enemy moving forward. A large force had collected to the east of Sevastopol and was moving down the Fedioukine Hills.

Their intention seemed to be to attack our supply base at Balaklava and then turn north and east to destroy our siege lines. To have any chance of achieving this they would almost certainly need to overcome the Highlanders.

The Turks all the while were receiving a massive artillery bombardment. After a while they took to their heels. This retreat was repeated all along their defensive position, as Turks in their dark blue, French style, brass buttoned tunics were seen running for their lives. Their blue-tasselled, red fezzes flying off in all directions.

"Look at 'em go, leaving our lads to it as usual," said Corporal Hislop, putting into words what many of us were thinking.

They paid dearly for this, however, as many of them were cut down by sabre and lance of the pursuing Cossacks.

To late to save the Turks came the order for the 1st and 4th Divisions to leave Sevastopol and go to the aid of Balaklava. Not General Hestitate again!

Soon, we witnessed the Russian cavalry move against Sir Colin Campbell's 93rd Highlanders. As we stood looking at the two ranks of kilted men, Sergeant-Major Reeves turned to rifleman Tremain and said, "What do you think of them, boy?"

"A fine sight, sir," he replied.

Tremain was no older than I had been when I had first joined the Brigade.

"Not only do they look good, but they fight good," continued the sergeant-major, "though a bit breezy when the wind blows up their kilts. Not like your trousers with all safely gathered in and kept nice and snug."

The rifleman looked puzzled.

"Must move about a bit when the action starts," said Reeves with enthusiasm.

By now the enemy cavalry were closer and within moments were hurling themselves time and time again at the Scottish infantry. The Russians just could not break through that thin, scarlet-clad line.

We then saw the red-coated Heavy Brigade at the charge as they moved in to support the 93rd. They managed to turn the Russian horse and push them back down the North Valley.

Sitting nearby, watching these events unfold, were the blue tunics of the Light Brigade, probably wishing it was them and not the Heavies pushing the enemy back. From our vantagepoint on the slopes of the Causeway Heights, but where, because of the range, we were really ineffective against the Russian gunners to the north, south and end of the valley, we spotted a lone horseman in the uniform of the 11th Hussars galloping down the slope towards the Light Brigade.

Captain Fortune glanced at his watch, "Just after 11:15," he announced to no one in particular.

After a few moments delay, accompanied by a lot of very energetic arm waving and pointing, the Light Brigade with the lone messenger at their head set off at walking pace down the North Valley towards the Russian guns about a mile away. This seemed to us on the Heights a very risky, if not foolhardy and forlorn action to take. The box-shape they were riding into was lined with guns and the muskets and rifles of enemy infantry. What could horses, sabres and lances do against shot and shell?

***

The advancing English cavalry moved from a walk to a gallop. While from the valley's end the first round of shot began to find its first targets. Fire from the two sides then began to take its toll. As flame and smoke belched from Russian guns and muskets, Hussars and their mounts began to fall. I saw several men's heads smashed from their bodies. One man's horse continuing with the dead, headless body still upright in the saddle at the charge.

This was a magnificent, though hopeless scene. We were powerless to help as more and more horses and men crashed to earth. Our cheers that had greeted the start of their attack gave way to a stunned silence. Cavalry always seemed to regard themselves as a cut above the rest of the army. They were certainly paid more than us, but this was different, this was a horrible sight; we were witnessing murder.

A few of the Light Brigade did manage to reach the Russian

guns. They even managed to kill and wound numbers of Russian gunners.

Then the survivors of the first wave, the 13th Light Dragoons and 17th Lancers, started to turn and make their way back up the valley. By now the 11th Hussars, 8th Hussars and 4th Light Dragoons were having to take notice of the men returning and the many riderless horses. It was a glorious, brave spectacular, chaotic sight, no doubt applauded by the ladies and other people watching from the safety of the Sapoune Heights.

Russian cavalry, waiting at the valley's end, also seemed to be in some confusion. It looked as though they had been sent forward to protect their guns, but instead, had moved off as the Light Brigade charged around their artillery pieces and in their direction. Perhaps the Russians like us had been stunned and surprised by the charge. Surely no cavalry would be that inclined to suicide to charge guns at point-blank range. The charge, then so unexpected, had caught them unawares, though it had taken seven long minutes for the Light Brigade to reach the guns. We had applauded as the shock of the daring charge had sent Cossacks crashing into their own infantry. Such was the confusion the Light Brigade had caused.

Off to our left, the first of the returning Brigade had reached roughly their starting point. Exhausted, stunned men began to slide from their saddles. A party of Russian cavalry had abandoned its rather half-hearted pursuit of the returning Light Brigade. Instead, they were attacking the much easier quarry of clumps of wounded men who lay scattered in the valley.

We managed to shoot and kill a few of them as they rode within range of our rifles in their cold-blooded enthusiasm to get at our unhorsed and wounded cavalrymen.

We were then ordered back to camp, and, as we skirted the Sapoune Hill, we heard the excited chatter of spectators as they made their way back to their quarters by carriage and horseback.

"What sort of people turn out to see men been cut to pieces, as though it was a day at the races or hunting a fox?" asked rifleman Buxton.

"The same types who would have cheered Christians bein' thrown to the lions in old Roman times," answered Captain Fortune in a very acid tone.

***

Very early the next morning, the 26th October, we paraded and were told that the Russians had marched a strong force out of Sevastopol to attack Mount Inkerman. They were heading straight for the 2nd Division's camp at Home Ridge. It turned out that we were not after all needed, as a force from that same Division had managed to hold them long enough for artillery to arrive and scatter them. I thought we had been very lucky, as our forces seemed to be spread thinly across the Heights. Especially as we soon received word that a strong reinforcement of Russians was heading towards the northern part of Sevastopol. Again, rumours did most of the talking as estimates were putting the strength of Prince Menschekov's force at the best part of one hundred thousand.

English infantrymen, although hampered by very heavy rain during the first few days of November, had managed to dig some defensive positions known as the Sandbag Battery and just south of it was the Barrier. This, it was hoped, would either persuade the enemy not to move against these positions or if they did, give early warning of any movement that might mean an all out attack was about to take place by the Russians from the north. This attack could then be stopped from turning south and west against us besieging Sevastopol. As far as the eye could see, hundreds of extra pickets were stationed to ensure our lines were secure. It was suggested that companies of riflemen would act as Russians in a mock attack just north of these newly created bastions, just to see how effective they were and how alert the defenders would be against a surprise attack. The date we were given to make this foray was Sunday, the 5th November but others, it turned out, had rather more immediate and more realistic and deadly plans.

On Saturday, 4th November, at around three in the morning, a strong force of the enemy was reported as leaving Sevastopol and moving along the Careenage Ridge against my battalion's left flank. Then they turned towards Shell Hill, which was a very narrow ridge. A company of we riflemen had taken up a position nearby, ready to disperse on the Sunday for our mock attack on the Sandbag Battery. A fortunate thing about the whole timing of the Russian attack was that, after all that recent rain, their progress would be very difficult as leather boots would be slipping and sliding on the ridge's rocky surface.

It was then reported that another enemy force had crossed the Charnaya River and was climbing the heights above the Inkerman Bridge. Fortunately for us also, was the presence of fog, which helped us by slowing down their advance. It did though, serve to hamper our forward pickets from hearing and seeing their moving along the rain sodden ridge. A force of five or six thousand did manage to push our side back. The noise of artillery and rifle fire, its direction masked by the fog did cause some confusion in the 2nd Division's camp. Men and horses rushed around as they prepared to counter-attack the unseen Russian force along the ridge. The messenger sent to us to find out what was happening and from where, was duly informed and he returned to the 2nd Division's camp. General de Lacy Evans sent out extra pickets into the fog to locate the exact position of the attackers. The enemy were certainly gaining ground. Men, not able to see each other in the swirling mist, began to fire where they thought the Russians were. Riflemen did as well! Then the Russians seemed to be hesitating and suddenly did not seem to be pressing on with their attack on the defences. They could have been waiting the arrival of reinforcements. Runners from our pickets told us that a strong Russian force, probably the reinforcements, had not climbed to the Inkerman Heights. Had they advanced in their three columns and joined their countrymen then we would have all, almost certainly, been pushed back and probably defeated once and for all.

As it was, very hard fighting took place around the Sandbag Battery. There were fierce hand-to-hand engagements as this position changed ownership many times.

***

All around us we could hear the hissing of shells, the mingling of bugle calls with shouting, the clash of bayonet on bayonet and the pinging of bullets on rocks. In this heated battle, charge and counter-charge was repeated time and again with soldiers just hacking away at anything. Men fired on their own side. Perhaps, had the Russians not hesitated they might have pushed us out of the battery rather than traded it with us so often and at such high cost.

General Raglan at some point must have sent for French help as he watched from the Sapoune Heights. Soon Zouaves, who seemed perfectly at home fighting in this sort of terrain, arrived. Off they rushed, across rocky, scrub-covered hills, yelling and firing their Minié rifles. The enemy fell back from the Sandbag Battery then into the Quarry Ravine, which by then was overflowing with Russians. Again, the general confusion meant they began to fire into their own men desperately trying to get away from the Zouave charge. The French reached the Battery where the English survivors of concentrated Russian attacks had almost reached breaking point. The Guards were down to barely one hundred men. With a company of riflemen and the advance of Zouaves we were able to intervene in time. Everywhere, Russians seemed to be in full retreat as the allies poured accurate rifle fire at them. Hundreds of them were killed and many trampled on, as they headed back and tried to re-cross the bridge. Many more were then drowned in the river.

The Frenchmen continued their hot pursuit. We learned later that a handful of them had pursued retreating Russians right into Sevastopol itself.

They found it almost deserted, as it seemed every available Russian had been mustered for the attack or had been sent to reinforce the south-facing bastions just in case the allies were able to take advantage, and send a force in to take the town while the action around the ruins of Inkerman was unfolding. There seemed to be little hope of our commander-in-chief encouraging such inititive. Later, it was reported that these adventurers had even reached the quay, looting as they went. It did not end well though for the Frenchmen, as some of them for some unfathomable reason had taken a boat, but were killed by a direct hit as they crossed Sevastopol Harbour.

***

One question was on many soldiers minds, not least mine; Williams put it in his usual joyless tone, "If these dozy, Froggie bastards can do it, then why can't we just walk in?"

After this battle of Inkerman, stock was taken of our losses. We had, in all over 2,500 killed and wounded. This included Rifle Brigade casualties of one officer killed, two wounded, five sergeants and twenty-two killed and over thirty wounded. One of our men was taken prisoner. French losses were about 1,700 killed and wounded with Russian losses at over 10,000. All these casualties during not much more than about four hours of fighting, but very intense fighting.

Once again we were given the job, along with other regiments, of burying the dead. I was one of seven other sergeants given the honour of carrying off the body of General Cathcart, who had been shot in the heart. His body though showed signs of him having received many bayonet wounds.

It also looked as though looters had stripped him of personal items, including his fine silver watch we had often seen him with in South Africa. He was buried on that hill that became Cathcart's Hill.

Bodies, especially of Russians, lay in heaps all around the Battery and down to and in Quarry Ravine. Underneath the dead there were many wounded in the most distressing of conditions. All over were headless bodies, legs cut off from the groin, arms sometimes in a tunic sleeve that looked completely untouched. Some men had smashed chests, others had stomachs and intestines spilling out. Lots more showed signs of the intensive use of bayonets. There were also men screaming in pain. Yet others called on their God. Russians, someone's sons, pressed icons to their lips while many called for their mothers in their dire hour of need.

***

For several days, the burying of the dead took up most of our time. As we took bodies away, once more the scavengers descended on this unhappy scene and removed trophies from the dead and dying. Many icons and crosses, some just ripped from still living hands, would soon be finding their way into a new home in the withdrawing rooms of England. We did notice that some of the Russians seemed to be the worse for drink, confirming what some of our officers had thought about the way they had behaved during the many attacks around the Sandbag Battery. It was true they received a generous daily ration of vodka. Who could blame them though. They seemed to always hurl themselves into battle.

Another suggestion regarding their zeal was that their priests had been stirring them up to such extremes of fighting anger in retaliation for the way they said allied soldiers had defiled their churches. Fortified by this and strong drink or not they had certainly been energetic and frenzied in their assaults. Stories also gradually emerged regarding their day to day treatment. They often had little choice in joining the army. Service was long. Punishments were very severe and officers treated them badly, far worse than even in our army. They seemed to be little more than cannon fodder to be slaughtered for the Tsar. Men were threatened if they did not fight.

Their many dead bodies now lay in ragged mounds as proof of their brave but desperate efforts.

It seemed that it would take a long time before the Russians bothered to ask to clear their casualties from in and around the battleground where I had certainly taken part in some of the bloodiest hand-to-hand fighting. A Coldstream Guard sergeant standing a few paces from me, removed his battered bearskin, mopped his brow, waved an arm at the devastation before us and said, "Warm, deadly work, eh, sarge?"

"Yeh, let's hope this gets us into the town before too long. Surely they can't take much more of this punishment, can they?"

"Neither can we. They cut us to ribbons!"

Our gaze was then held by the contorted faces and bodies twisted in the agony of death of dozens of Russians, and we lapsed into silence.

Then, thankfully, we received orders for the Russians to be buried as well as our own. It was cold, which helped keep down the smell of blood and decay. We helped dispose of thousands, but others still lay on the side of the hill for days to come. During the days that followed, the French began to take over the defences on Mount Inkerman. It seemed to me, and I never thought I would admit such a thing, that as they had brought the larger force to the Crimea and had saved the day at the Battery on those muddy, slippery slopes, then they deserved to take it over. As Williams put it, "they're bloody welcome to it."

After our success at Inkerman on that Sunday, there seemed once more to follow what was fast becoming the habit of not following up victory. Regardless of yet another win, no further advance was going to be made on Sevastopol. This was all the more worrying now that winter was about to coldly embrace our rather exposed lines. It seemed likely that the English commander, milord Raglan, was going to keep us on the Heights and resume the offensive in the spring. It was not his ample backside that would be wet and freezing in the siege lines, just thousands of ours.

First Alma, then Balaklava and now Inkerman, but very little to show for our efforts other than cholera, dysentery, casualties and a growing weariness. More stories circulated, but this time they mentioned that officers in some regiments were about to return home. We had once again beaten a larger force and gained nothing, but what was the response? Nothing! So some of the officers decided they would just leave.

Not all of them bothered to come back; if only we could do the same.

During the morning of the 9th November, around 7 p.m. we were sent as covering party to Inkerman. Entrenching work by Turks was going on to make a redoubt. The officer commanding this working party, Colonel Smith of the 68th, ordered our two companies to form an extended line of pickets in front of the position, which overlooked ravines and ridges where yet another likely Russian attack might begin.

6

By the beginning of the second week of November, we began
to feel the real bite of winter. For three days and three nights
we shivered in our tents. Freezing winds and rain swept across
the Heights above Sevastopol. We huddled together, helpless
in the mud as the rain continued to pour down and through
the bottom of our flimsy, summer issue tents. Then, very
early on the 14th November, a powerful hurricane ripped its
way across the Crimea. Our tents and most of our personal
equipment and kit were just picked up like flimsy autumn
leaves and flung far and wide. Even wagons, barrels, boxes and
trunks were pitched everywhere. As blankets and coats took
to the air, tables and chairs added to the general confusion.
Horses bolted and in their wide-eyed panic crashed through
an already disorderly camp. As men rushed around trying
to retrieve those items of kit and a few personal possessions,
falling trees and flying objects inflicted injuries on the
desperate foragers as they too were blown off their feet. A few
men died as a result of being hit by flying debris and from
exposure to the biting cold. Bits of houses, roof tiles, slates
and thatch added to the general mêlée.

Daylight bore witness to the full effects of the storm.
Everywhere was destruction, and the day was spent in mainly
fruitless attempts at bringing some order to our shattered camp.

Worse was to come. As evening approached, so did the
biting wind. Supplies were low and even the little we had was
now scattered far and wide.

The cavalry's horses were in much distress and close to starving.

The French, who seemed so much better prepared than we were, sent up many bales of hay. Parties of men were sent out to look for wood to build huts, but little that would be of any use was found. This was very serious as the cold, rain and snow-showers were making our lives thoroughly miserable. Hardly a surprise that our division now had nearly a quarter of its strength on the sick-list. The temperature continued to drop; snow flurries, then heavy rain gave way to snow. Men, fingers numbed with cold, tried desperately to re-pitch those tents that had been retrieved, but only to find many had great tears and holes in them. Other men just covered themselves with their Cathcart groundsheets and huddled against broken walls and rocky outcrops. Word came up that supplies that could have helped our dire situation had been lost as ships in the harbour had crashed into each other. Many were holed and took in water while other ships just sunk. Waves as high as the tallest of that forest of masts crashed down on to decks, and ships were thrown against rocks. Uniforms were lost as well as Minié rifles. The damage done by the storm, the shortage of supplies and the approach of winter promised only a very bleak future.

**

I accompanied Captain Fortune on a visit to one of the French camps. Although the storm had been just as bad for them in terms of weather, they seemed to be faring rather better. The men of the Imperial Guard Cavalry were wearing sheepskin and hooded cloaks. Much better than the sort of protection my greatcoat was giving me against the Russian climate. This whole situation reminded me very much of a picture I had seen in a book.

A little boy, very thin and dressed only in rags stood in front of a big, well fed, very well-dressed, comfortable-looking man.

The boy was asking for more of the rather thin gruel that was his main meal of the day. As I walked on into the French camp I felt very much like that little boy, especially as a smell of cooking was in the air and I was in a different uniform.

"We'll wander over there, Finchy," said my company commander.

We approached two women dressed in a sort of dark uniform serving, from what looked like ovens, hot food to a line of men. At this point we were joined by a French officer, Captain Didierjean. He was something of a friend of Captain Fortune's and the source of that little map.

"Ameriez-vous, diner?"

"Wants to know if we'd like some grub," said Captain Fortune.

"Well, I could probably manage just a morsel or two," I said, as my stomach groaned in anticipation.

Captain Fortune turned to the Frenchman – a member of the elite Guard, which also happened to be the very elite of the French army, the Cent-Gardes, as Captain Fortune later told me – and agreed that we would. At that, Monsieur Didierjean moved towards the mobile canteen. He was waved cheerfully forward by a French soldier, then rattled three plates, offered us one each and motioned us in front of him. Portions of an encouraging amount of food, a kind of beef stew, was ladled on to our plates. Our host grabbed some newly baked bread and led us towards a flat rock.

"Asseyez-vous, mes amis."

This was my first real hot food for many weeks.

"I don't suppose I could transfer to this regiment, sir?" I asked Captain Fortune.

"Probably not. We're runnin' a bit short of good men as it is," he replied, grinning.

The whole episode was a complete contrast to the daily scene in our camp. So many of our men across the Heights were hungry, too often shirtless and bootless, and shivering under a soaking blanket.

We were supposed to be given regularly, our own individual food ration with wood for fuel to cook it ourselves. This was not happening, and no real surprise that in many regiments' diarrhoea was widespread.

In some battalions the very few women, soldier's wives, who were allowed to accompany their husbands overseas did manage to do a very modest amount of cooking. They also did laundering and helped tend the sick. But they were too few in numbers to make any real difference. Though who would want to put their wife through such a campaign as this one was turning out to be?

As we returned from the French camp, Captain Fortune grudgingly admitted that the French were certainly better organised in most things, including the medical attention their men received, which, compared to what ours seemed to be receiving, would not be too difficult to achieve. And as for the food, we definitely could not compare.

***

"It seems they have been gettin' some ideas from a French cook at the Reform Club in London. Perhaps we could persuade him to come out to the Crimea and cook for us," said Fortune. "It will change though, and soon," he confided. "You know that reporter fellow? He's been sendin' reports home of how bad things have been here so far. Colonel Windham has also been askin' for changes. He seems to be a pretty decent sort of fellow and will get things done providin' he doesn't get in the way of too many horses hooves. Still, can't get much worse, can it?"

My company commander, unlike so many of his class, did have some idea of the shortages his men faced. There was usually a great gap between the officer class, many of them coming from very wealthy families owning a large house or even houses, estates to match and in control of armies of servants. They had largely bought their way into the military and had little or nothing in common with the men they commanded. These same men would have been bullied by the landed classes if they had worked on their estates or served in a large house. Some had exchanged that for soldiering and faced many similar restrictions. At the whim of a young gentleman not long out of public school, they could, under the Army's strict discipline, face a charge that could result in a flogging or hanging. Some of those officers would, I am sure, have been very disappointed when the number of strokes that could be applied at a flogging was reduced, a few years before, from I think about 2,000 to just fifty. Just fifty! This, for, perhaps, minor offences such as drunkenness.

And who hadn't at some time or another ended up the worse for drink in the ranks. Then, of course, between occasionally having their lives put at risk because of indecision and poor leadership by someone barely old enough to shave. Not that delays or blunders were limited to junior officers. Our experiences from the very beginning of this Russian campaign confirmed the views held in the lower ranks that incompetence ran from cornet to general.

Men who had faced the grim prospect of the workhouse, like the little boy and his gruel bowl, or had drifted into crime and eventually the hangman's rope could take the Queen's shilling. My earlier visit to London had shown me the dirt and squalor of parts of it and how easy it would be just to end up on the wrong side of the law. At least the 'choice' to join the army could be the only desperate option left for some men. At least they would have clothes (a uniform), pay (irregular at times), food (occasionally) and shelter (sometimes). They might, if they were really lucky, survive their service and then suffer old age, but content in the knowledge they had helped preserve, as the hymn 'All things Bright and Beautiful' has it, 'the rich man in his castle, The poor man at his door'. Not that many of the men above Sevastopol would be finding much that was bright, let alone beautiful in a cold, wind-swept camp. Not everything though was the fault of the weather, but no account had been taken of its effect on the men. Nor was any great effort being made, or so it seemed, to keep the army adequately fed and supplied.

Why were the French better served? Had revolutions showed what might happen if nothing was changed?

What was noticeable during my occasional visits to the French camp was there seemed to be less of a division between French officers and their men. Punishments were less barbaric and not so frequently given than in our own army, something that seemed to amuse the French; perhaps they regarded us as uncivilised!

***

During my time in London, I heard about the activities of a group called the Chartists who were intent on changing everyone's life. It seems that they caused quite a stir at the time, but then seemed to just fade away. I expect that for a while though they did put the wind up the upper classes.

Although Captain Fortune had originally bought his commission he was, in my opinion and that of others, a natural leader. I had also, always found him to be fair and he had treated me almost as an equal. Perhaps it was because we both came from the same part of Hampshire. He though, lived at Durford Hall while I lived in a cottage in the village of Lower Durford.

He had never to my knowledge during my service in the battalion started court martial proceedings towards a flogging. Though neither had most of the other officers in the Rifle Brigade. They tended to be closer to their men, often sharing rations and hardships alike. This was unlike some of their brother officers in other regiments. Some of them had 18th century views of the world and barely needed an excuse for such punishments.

Taking meals alongside their men tended to make for a

greater understanding between officers and riflemen when they were in the field. We had trained to work in small groups, often just in pairs, and were required to move and adapt to whatever the terrain without always being told to do so. This affected how we fought: other regiments often relied on a volley of rifle or musket fire from massed ranks, whereas riflemen were expected to fire at individual targets.

Captain Fortune told us that his father had witnessed this style of attack at Waterloo, recalling especially the failure of Napoleon's Imperial Guard to just roll over English ranks as volley after volley took their toll of the advancing Frenchmen.

Many officers in the battalion even encouraged competition and might offer small prizes for consistently accurate shooting in the rifle butts. This certainly brought our officers closer to their men.

We all carried out the usual drills on the parade ground, though not as gaily coloured as some, but it was our skills at getting ahead of the infantry at a quick pace in skirmishing lines that marked us out as a special unit.

Captain Fortune had originally joined another regiment, but when a vacancy arose and because his father had fought at Waterloo in 1815 and before that in the Peninsula with the old 95th, he joined what had become the Rifle Brigade.

James Fortune's father had been in the thick of the fighting in June, 1815. The story was well known around the estate and surrounding villages.

His regiment held off wave after wave of French attacks, including that of Napoleon's Imperial Guard. And now here was his son fighting forty years later, but this time on the same side of another French emperor, Napoleon III's soldiers. A shell had burst to the left of Colonel Fortune and a splinter had hit him high up on his cheekbone. It had bounced into this left eye, sliced his eyelid, split his eyebrow and lodged just above it. This wound had left him with a vivid 'Z'-shaped scar, which did nothing to improve his looks or general demeanour. During his time on the bench, many a wrongdoer had more than one reason for gasping in fear as sentences were handed down.

My early life as part of a large family sharing a small cottage owned by Lord Durford had been, like so many, quite difficult. My father worked on the estate, but during winters and at other times when the weather was bad, or a slump in prices, or poor harvests then food could be scarce. He had, earlier in his life, been the baker and when his back injury would allow he still helped out there. Somehow we managed to get by. As I grew up I was lucky in being taught to read and write in a little schoolroom at the back of the village church. My mother told me that I was a very fortunate boy, as the 'big house' had made some sort of payment towards my education. Not that this stopped the vicar's wife from constantly telling me that it was her Christian duty to help the poor and that I should remember my place and be grateful. There were two or three other 'grateful' members of the little class but I seemed to have a talent for learning and my reading and writing thrived.

Books though were few and far between to begin with and I took to reading anything, even the Bible.

The fact that I was the eldest, though not by much, of all the children in my family also meant I would be needed to work before I was much older. Not that we children didn't already do our share; there was always sewing, spinning, weaving, mending clothes, cutting wood, picking wild fruits, feeding a couple of pigs, helping at harvest time in the fields and helping my father when he could, mother and a brother in the bakery. Another brother, George, helped make brooms for the village and the hall.

When my father was the baker, until he injured his back, the family lived in the bakery, but after, we moved into the cottage.

The bakery was close to a small brewery in the village. Wheat ground in the watermill provided the flour for the bakery.

During the days when I wasn't in the school room and from about the age of nine, I helped out in the bakery as well as other odd jobs alongside my brother Tom, who my parents said was about the same age as me!

Yet things seemed to be changing all around us. Some of the villagers had left to look for work in the nearby towns like Portsmouth, Southampton and Winchester. According to the vicar, the waterwheel, turning that wheat from the fields into flour, had existed since olden times. The bakery used the froth from the top of the beer or the scrapings at the bottom of the newly brewed liquid to add to the flour and salt, which was then kneaded into dough in wooden troughs.

After weighing the dough into 2-pound chunks it was baked in the oven. From a very early lark-like start in the morning from collecting the beer froth, bringing the ground wheat from the mill in sacks weighing twice as any man. Making the dough, raking out the embers of the fire for each of the five or six bread bakings, my day helping was very long, usually about nine hours. Kneading, a back-breaking job in itself, helping to carry the large flour bags to the kneading troughs, swabbing the floors of ash from the fire, meant that by the time I was twelve or thirteen I was quite strong. The bakery was open seven days a week, all year round, save Christmas Day, May Day, Easter Day and for the Harvest Festival when most of the village shared bread, fruit, beer and music from the fiddle player.

Bread had to be delivered around the village. A pack full of 2-pound loaves on my back was no easy task in sun, rain or snow. Most villagers bought the ordinary household bread for about 4d a loaf. I also made deliveries of loaves; the Coburg loaf, consisting of the finest flour and weighing 4 pounds, to the hall, the vicarage and Doctor Mallinson's at a cost of 9d a loaf.

Changes had started in other counties in the early 1830s. There had been riots, apparently led by a Captain Swing, in the way machines were forcing labourers off the land. Then, when

I was nine or ten years of age, the first of a number of poor harvests forced wheat prices up. Not everyone in my village could afford the price of bread, which doubled in price. Other, cheaper grains, such as barley, were used to make bread, but this was still too much for some people to pay.

Our bakery had to cut down the number of loaves it produced. Some very poor people were forced to leave. Wages had not gone up with the price of bread. Loaves and rents had increased, but a farm labourer's wages in 1850 was still about what it had been ten or so years before, about nine shillings and sixpence a week. No job, no work, no money, and no bread!

Not only was the work at this time, for those who had some, hard, but it was beginning to be less regular and my wages were cut as I approached my thirteenth birthday. I began to think about what else I could do.

The next couple of years seemed to drift away. I was still in the bakery, but ready to turn my hand to anything else that cropped up. I even managed to keep up with some reading. Then, after my fourteenth birthday I found more regular employment and better wages assisting a butcher. The snag was that it was in Winchester. It was a lively city, at least that's how it seemed after a life spent in my quiet village that seemed to be steadily becoming quieter still, as villagers drifted away in search of work elsewhere.

***

As I had a very early start each day, I slept in a small outhouse below which was where the butcher slaughtered most of the animals he then sold on in the shop. I walked the five or six miles or so home, with some unsold pies and sausages late on Saturday afternoon. I began my working week by walking back to the city late on Sunday afternoon ready for Monday morning. Very occasionally, my journey to and from the village coincided with a wagon going my way.

My wages of ten shillings and fourpence were much better than a labourer's on the estate, but were not likely in the long run to make my fortune. I managed though not to spend too much, could give my mother some and even save a modest amount.

I coped with the long hours, very early starts to each day and the walk to and from Lower Durford in all weathers, but as weeks merged into months I began to yearn for something else. At odd times I managed to widen my reading and even bought a few used books from a bookshop near the Cathedral when I walked past on my rounds delivering meat from my barrow to the large houses in and around the city. This reading was opening up a whole new world, and over one Saturday evening, I talked to my parents about my need for a change. They were only too aware that many families and many sons had already been forced to leave in search of work. I know that I had work, but had to do something else.

A very sad incident finally made up my mind. One of my brothers worked for a fruit-seller in Romsey. I set off for Mr Giffard's shop, intending to buy some apples from those he kept in the loft above the shop, and then walk the short distance home. It was a cold day with the promise of snow in the grey-blue sky. I reached the shop but found it shut and my brother standing outside, sobbing.

"What's to do, Fred?" I called out, wondering why the stalls with the other things the shop sold were not on the trestles that usually groaned under the weight of pots, pans, brooms and everything else, as well as fruit and vegetables, Mr Giffard sold.

"Little 'un scalded himself with a pot of boiling tea water. Not expected to last the day. I'm to go home and will come back tomorrow."

I put an arm round my brother's shoulders and we set off at a brisk pace towards Lower Durford. We reached the cottage and

Fred told our parents of the accident to the eighteen-month-old Giffard child. How had he managed to get so close to the hob and pull the teapot down on himself? Poor lad must have been in agony when he died. A sad business like this made up my mind that life was too short and it was the spur that decided me to leave. Next stop, London. Though not after being warned about the dangers and vices that could befall an innocent lad in the nation's capital. I could hardly wait! I did wonder how they knew as neither of my parents had strayed any further than Winchester in the whole of their lives.

**

A week later, I was buying a third class railway ticket from Southampton to a station in London named after the Duke of Wellington's victory at Waterloo over Napoleon I in 1815.

The capital was teeming with life of every description. Wagons, Hackney-coaches, broughams of every size jostled for space along crowded roads. Some parts of the city like Belgravia, Grosvenor Square, Hanover Square and Berkeley Square contained very large houses with liveried servants jumping to attention at every turn as master or mistress issued their orders. Tailors, bakers, grocery boys, traders of every type delivered items of every description, but to the 'tradesmen' entrance, not up the marble steps complete with painted iron railings to a very impressive front door. Of an evening came the ladies in flowing dress and gentlemen elegantly clothed and top-hatted to the opera or theatre, while other gentlemen had their clubs or other entertainments and smartly dressed, available women at the Haymarket.

Then there were the poorer parts of the thriving metropolis, such as Spitalfields, Hounsditch, Whitechapel and on around the docks at Wapping, Poplar and Limehouse. Drunken beggars, the blind, the crippled, prostitutes old and young were everywhere in these poorer districts jostling with thin, ragged men, women and children barely existing in their hovels or 'living' on those streets.

***

During my first night in London, I had been forced to rest on a bench in Green Park, but slept little as all kinds of life passed by and I feared for my bundle and the hard-earned coins in my pocket. The next day I went in search of lodgings and found a room in a boarding house between Whitechapel and Poplar. This lodging, though barely adequate for human habitation, served me while I took jobs in the eastern part of the capital and was well-placed for Smithfield and the East India Docks. Later, I moved to Westminster where my lodgings were still modest, but for my four shillings and sixpence a week I did have a bed and two small meals each day. This was bread of a dubious quality, cheese, and tea in a large cup and occasionally meat . Like elsewhere among London's seething masses, when the rain was heavy there was that unmistakable smell of sewage.

What drains there were just could not cope with surplus water and human waste. Though in some parts of London animal and human waste was hoarded and sold to farmers. Every so often I sought the comforting warmth of a 2d bath near Trafalgar Square while keeping a very wary eye on money and clothes.

The very next day after arriving in London I had gone off in search of work and found myself at the docks. There were jobs, mostly just day to day work, and I tried my hand at quite a few different things, including time at the East India Docks, several weeks at Smithfield and others that only required muscle rather than brains. At least this allowed me to pay my rent and eat, though not always well, but regularly enough to keep me from starving like the thin, wide-eyed souls forced to beg in the gutters.

Some families kept cows, pigs and other livestock in and around their poor dwellings, adding to that general smell that hung over much of the capital. I could have been sitting in one of the cottages, some little more than hovels, shared with the animals on the edge of my own village with that all too familiar air attacking my nose. Not much hope either in the way of streets paved with gold yet London and all the big towns attracted desperate people.

After a while I decided to move from exploring on foot to trying the river and walked in the direction of Vauxhall, my pace quickening as I caught sight of steamers on the Thames. My start that morning had been an early one. I had all my life risen with the lark and as I made my way down to the landing stage I was passed by other early risers rushing off to their work.

I handed over my one penny and was swept up the gangplank along with the other passengers and on to the deck, rather more eagerly anticipating my first ever time on a river paddle steamer than those who did the journey every day. This from Vauxhall to London Bridge carried sober, young, earnest-looking and quite well-dressed men on their way to offices and banks in the City. They crowded the deck alongside the shabbier-clothed workers in all sorts of trades. Although this was my first experience of a steamboat it was certainly not going to be my last. I watched with some fascination as the paddle wheels on the sides of the boat splashed around and pushed the boat through the murky water. Interesting, too, was the small boy, the call boy, who stood halfway up the paddle wheel box in a kind of harness to prevent him being devoured by the paddles or drowned in the waters thrashing angrily below. At intervals, the captain of the steamer shouted instructions to the boy who in turn called them out below to the engine room. The boat's decks were painted black and I quessed that the same colour was used on the iron hull. Its funnel was also black but with a single red stripe around its middle. In large white letters painted on the square paddle-box, I read The City Steamboat Company.

All around us were craft of every sort: steamers large and small, sleek-looking three-masted sailing ships that looked as though they could go at a fast clip and steam ships towing barges with all manner of goods from hay and straw to provide for the thousands of horses in the capital to grain and stone for building and coal.

Then there were the watermen in their skiffs and wherries trying desperately to keep hold of their trade against new, quicker, steam-driven traffic as well as avoiding being swamped by them. It was very obvious how quickly a paddle steamer could turn, as the two paddles were provided with their power by two separate engines. This fact was not lost on the smaller boats, as sharp turns were made without warning on a very busy river.

As we approached some of the bridges during our progress along the Thames, the funnel, which reminded me of an open mouth at its end, had to be lowered. This showered us all in sparks, smoke and dust.

At last the journey was over and we travellers streamed off the boat and over London Bridge in the direction of St Paul's Cathedral and then on towards Smithfield. Here cattle, sheep and pigs vied with carts, carriages of every sort, horses and walkers. Traffic came to a stop. Nothing moved for some minutes until the drovers moved the animals on towards the market. I hadn't quite expected to be dodging various piles of animal waste in the capital. It certainly wasn't gold that some of London's streets were lined with. The noise was also near-deafening. Traffic, hoarse calls of costermongers and every kind of stall and shopkeeper, small armies of navvies repairing roads with picks and shovels and heavy mallets to lay large granite blocks. Upon this surface they tipped a dark mixture to form a black cap over the width of the road. This helped water drain off and give wheeled traffic a less bumpy ride.

Weaving in and out of yet more men, women and children going about their daily business were men wearing boards on their chests and backs.

Sandwich boards advertised all manner of goods and services. Maids with buckets, small pails and cows offered fresh milk to passers-by and boys sent on errands for their employers' coffee.

I headed towards the rather squalid Leicester Square and, feeling rather overwhelmed by the sights, sounds and smells during my tour, I decided to head back in the direction of my lodgings at Westminster. I caught a horse-drawn omnibus – another new experience – that stated its ultimate destination was Chelsea. The red-liveried omnibus took twelve passengers inside and after they had climbed up the eight or ten metal rings that served as stairs, a further eight more on top. I watched with great interest and some amusement as a woman wearing a dress prepared to climb the primitive stepladder on the outside of the conveyance. Several passers-by, men, waited hopefully and watched in anticipation as her attempts at going up in the world might reveal her undergarments. The conductor at this point asked if any gentleman would care to give up his seat inside for one up above. I, gallantly I thought, took what would have been her place while she took mine after thanking me. After climbing up and sitting I thrust my hands deeply into my pockets to feel the comforting presence of my coins. I had been warned that omnibuses were a great source of income for pickpockets.

The omnibus moved off and took a pleasant if lazy route along the Haymarket, down Pall Mall, St James' Street, Piccadilly, skirting Green Park and Buckingham Palace Gardens and into Grosvenor Place. I got down from the omnibus at Victoria and reached my lodgings in the late afternoon.

***

After putting in a few more weeks' hard work I decided to take another day exploring London. This time I would go further downstream. I walked to London Bridge and on what was called the Surrey side was leaning against a rail under one of the bridge's many arches. While waiting for the steamer still some minutes from the jetty I glanced into the river. One thing I was certain about and that was how different it was to the river, a tributary of the Test that ran through the millrace in my own village. My river was clear and even in the shallow stretches, all manner of life could be found. There were no sticklebacks or trout in the thick, dark, rather foul water of London's main waterway. Our river could be swum in, but fall into the Thames and the filth would get to you before you drowned. Life rushed in a frenzy above, but below, I doubted there was anything living.

By now the squat-looking steamer had tied up and was taking passengers. All around the banks of the river other steamers were also plying their trade. I handed over my penny coin and a voice announced, "London Bridge to Woolwich," as we moved off towards whatever there was at Woolwich.

I had little clue where I was going, but it began to dawn on me as the sun appeared from behind white clouds that, perhaps for the first time in my life, I was free to please myself. I had a little money, lodgings, plain food and was no longer bound to parents, the village estate, the bakery, the butcher's in Winchester or to Lord Durford at the big house.

Yet I did not want to just recklessly throw away that freedom. This city, as my parents had said, contained every kind of vice there probably was. I did have the good fortune of being able to choose my path. Many all around and at home did not.

The steamer had continued on its way, passing docks, the East India I had seen on an earlier journey and had also worked there. Then there were the sad, drab rows of rickety tenements and dwellings on both sides of the river that condemned too many people to poverty.

"The next stop, the Warren Royal Arsenal," a voice called.

A few of the passengers, dressed in shabby grey clothes, scurried off in the direction of some large buildings set back some distance from the river.

I did not venture very far though and paid another penny for the return journey to London Bridge. An idea was gradually beginning to take form in my head.

Time, like the Thames, seemed to be floating by and thoughts began to drift back to my meeting with Lieutenant Fortune in the library of Durford Hall. London was proving a little disheartening; I hadn't expected those gold-paved streets of my storybooks, but didn't want to wish my life away. Perhaps the army would give me the adventure I desired and some purpose for my life.

7

It had been early August 1850 when I decided I must do something definite. By chance I had noticed two Chelsea Pensioners going into a public house not too far away from my lodgings in Westminster. Giving them a few minutes to settle, I went in and bought them each a drink. Pleased they had someone new to regale with their stories, they offered me a seat in a corner where I was rather wedged in and so became something of a captive listener. Stories poured out of fighting the French across Portugal, Spain and finally at Waterloo.

After about an hour of feeling as though I was marching alongside them as they remembered old campaigns and reducing my stock of coins, I weakly asked, "How do I get to join the Rifle Brigade?"

"Ah, the old 95th. No, what you want, lad, is my old regiment, the 52nd," one of them said.

"No," said the other, "there's nothing to touch the Brigade of Guards."

"We'll warrant that the 95th aren't that bad," added the first old soldier and they both looked at each other and nodded in agreement.

"They were between us at Waterloo, the old 95th, as the Imperial Guard marched towards us. Now there was a sight, boy, and that was a real battle."

"No, it must be the Rifles," I repeated.

Very reluctantly, they suggested I go off to the other side of the district and look for a public house with a dark green painted sign with a golden bugle and two crossed rifles.

It was called the 'Volunteer Rifleman.'

"We've seen a recruiting sergeant in there on a couple of times most weeks. Try there."

I thanked them and, with their 'good lucks' ringing in my ears, left them to their beer.

Half an hour later I found what I was looking for.

"Look where you're going, boy," said a tall, fair-haired fellow about my age, in an accent that I had not heard before and was perhaps a little more musical than my rather broad Hampshire one.

"You mind out yourself. I was here first," I replied.

I would discover some time later that he came from the county of Norfolk and that we would both serve in South Africa as riflemen, later as sergeants of the 1ˢᵗ Battalion, Rifle Brigade. Only occasionally did our paths cross because we served in different companies.

From signing a paper and swearing an oath of allegiance, everything seemed to move very quickly.

In December 1851, I was at Dover camp, having completed training. My company at morning parade was told to prepare for service in Cape Colony, South Africa.

On the 30ᵗʰ March 1852, over 700 officers and men, including me, came ashore through the surf at Algoa Bay, Cape of Good Hope from *HM Steamship Megaera*. This was to be my first adventure, but it could easily have been my last.

We later learned that we were originally supposed to be sailing from Portsmouth on *HMS Birkenhead*. Our commanding officer, however, refused to allow our battalion to be split between other ships. We stayed together, while most of those men on the *Birkenhead* were either drowned or taken by sharks when it foundered.

This ship had been one of the first of the navy's iron-hulled ships. It had originally been commissioned as a frigate and named

HMS Vulcan with two steam driven paddle-wheels. It was then re-named and changed to being a troop carrier and had set off from Portsmouth bound for South Africa. After landing some women and children in February 1852 at Cape Town, it had continued towards Algoa Bay. It then struck rocks eighty-five miles out from the first landing point. Soldiers paraded on deck as women and children boarded the lifeboats. Only a little over 190 survived out of the 643 soldiers on board. We were informed of these tragic events at a morning parade. The news was numbing but I felt relief at escaping their fate and admiration for the soldiers for their sacrifice in equal measure. Later my company commander also told us that, at the court martial held on board *HMS Victory* in May 1852, no one was blamed for the tragedy.

At that parade back in Dover the year before, I was pleased that one of my reasons for joining the Brigade was coming together, for one of the officers was that same Lieutenant Fortune and we had met several times before.

I recall around my thirteenth birthday, carrying some loaves in my backpack, from the village bakery up to Durford Hall.

I was told by my mother, who had taken the loaves freshly baked from the ovens herself, that I would be given something to bring back, so I must wait up at the big house. As was usual, I made my way to the side of the house where the servants' entrance to the kitchen was situated. I knocked on the door.

A kitchen maid opened the door and asked me what my business was with my elders and betters. I waved a loaf at her and was told to enter.

"Down there, on that chair, and mind you behave and don't pinch anything."

At that she scooped up the loaves and swept out of the room. Everywhere seemed very quiet. Ten minutes passed, but I was still waiting and quite alone.

I decided to explore and wandered into a large room, filled wall to wall and floor to ceiling with books.

One particular volume caught my attention: *Sketches by Boz* by Charles Dickens. It was full of short stories with simple pictures. I sat cross-legged on the floor and began to read. In a few minutes I was lost in my reading. I barely heard a door to the library open. The tall, lean figure of Lieutenant James Algernon Fortune strode into the room in a dark green uniform that looked almost black in the fading light of the day. Had we been in a wood on the estate, I might not have seen him against the leaves and branches of the trees.

"It's Jack Finch, ain't it?" he enquired pleasantly.

His tone was very different to what would have been the case had I been discovered by one of the servants, or worse still, by his father. Lord Durford's reputation as a flog, jail or hang 'em first and ask questions later kind of person was well known across the county. During his earlier life he had seemed to make it his ambition while serving on the bench to hang or populate the convict colony of New South Wales by his enthusiasm in transporting felons.

James Fortune sat down at a large, polished table.

"Not poachin' fish today then, just books, eh, Jack?" he said.

"No, sir, I wasn't going to steal anything, honest. I was just reading. I am very sorry for coming into your room. I meant no harm, sir."

"You read then? Course you do. You go for your lessons at the village church, don't you?"

"Yes sir, when I can and don't have to work."

"What's that you're readin'?" he asked.

"*Sketches by Boz*, by Charles Dickens."

"All a bit gloomy for me is Dickens. Seen this?" he said, taking a leather-bound volume from a small, very highly polished side table.

"*Oliver Twist*," I said. "No, sir, don't get much chance to read at home."

"It's an even gloomier tale of a poor lad. Comes good in

the end though. Perhaps it will for you too," he added, his eyes sparkling with humour in the light of a candle.

"I must go and so must you, but I'll see if we ain't got a few old books lyin' about that you could borrow."

He left the room with me staring after him. It was not the first time that I had encountered James when I had been caught in the wrong place. I had seen most of the Fortunes at one time or another when I was growing up. This was usually at church where they sat in their family's stall rather far removed from the poorer classes at the other end of church. It would also be fair to say that ordinary villagers went to church less and less as the years went by. I had also seen James Fortune a few times swimming in the river and in the pool below where I had on one occasion been attempting to catch fish. On most of the times I had seen him he had been with friends from his public school.

At times though one or other of the family would drop into the church school. On more than one of their visits, though I may have been mistaken, I had the feeling they were talking about me, but why would they be doing that? I decided I must have been imagining it.

Several years before James had found me in the library, he had come upon me suddenly as I sat by the river, fishing.

"Any luck?" he had asked.

"No, sir," I replied, fearing the thrashing to come as I was, I suppose, trying to poach.

"Who are you?"

"Jack Finch, sir," I said in a rather thin voice.

"Oh, so you're Jack Finch, are you? Well, we can't say you've been poachin' then, if you ain't caught anythin', can we?" And off he went with a wave of his arm.

That was my first and last attempt at catching fish from that river, but not the last time that I would sit on its bank. I wandered home but decided I would not tell my parents about what I considered was a lucky escape. I did though ask my mother a few questions about James Fortune, and was quite surprised when my mother seemed quite pleased that I was showing an interest.

"Mr. James is a fine young man and has just joined the army," she told me, "and when he can will join his father's old regiment."

She also said that his older brother, who would one day inherit the house and the estate, was in India as governor of one of that country's provinces.

8

After a week's lack of any great activity around Sevastopol, it was reported that several companies of Russian sharpshooters had occupied some old, ruined shepherds' huts and some caves. We called this position the 'Ovens' and of concern was the fact that from there the enemy was very easily able to fire on our batteries on Green Hill, as well as the French lines to our left.

Russian weapons were generally older and less reliable than ours. We had collected some of their weapons from the dead and found they still used many smooth bore muskets and even a few flintlocks. These sharpshooters would more likely have been issued with quite a good, accurate, rifled percussion musket, whose large calibre almost 0.7 inch packed quite a wallop. From their fire it seemed likely that sharpshooters did have these weapons in the caves and they were a dangerous distance, only some 200 yards away from our advanced positions.

The French general had requested that the English capture the new enemy offensive site. Three companies, including my own, were given the task of taking it from them.

The first we knew where we were going was when the officer in overall charge of the sortie marched us to the ravines. He then told us how we were to go about the attack. At 7:00 p.m. we were divided into two groups of fifty men with the remaining one hundred riflemen standing by ready to reinforce where needed. This reserve force was ordered to open fire.

The Russians returned their shots and showed the assault groups exactly where they were positioned.

One party, fifty strong, led by Lieutenant Tryon and a sergeant moved forward and was followed soon after by the second fifty, led by Lieutenant Axelby and a sergeant, me.

"Right, boys!" shouted the lieutenant. "Fix swords. Let's get among 'em."

Very soon we were charging straight at the Russians. By this time the reserves had ceased firing for fear of hitting the advancing riflemen.

We were on the Russians very quickly and before long engaged in hand-to-hand fighting, or more accurately bayonet-on-bayonet. Then our support joined the rest of us at the Russian positions. Enemy reserves began to fire at us; the darkness of the late November evening, the rocks and the pits fortunately giving us sufficient cover to prevent our sustaining great losses.

By and by we pushed the Russians back, but they did not give up the ground easily and made several attempts to retake the caves.

During this time I saw Lieutenant Tryon killed by a bullet to the head. Like Captain Fortune, he was well liked and respected by the men in his company and had fought extremely well at Inkerman on the 5th November.

The command of the sortie passed to another officer, Lieutenant Bourchier who very ably directed the defence of our newly captured position.

"Hang on, boys," shouted Lieutenant Axelby, "we've got them on the run. Let's keep it that way."

Just after dawn the next day another company of the battalion relieved us. As well as Lieutenant Tryon, eight riflemen were also killed and a further sixteen wounded.

Several days later at morning parade, a General Order was read out to us, which thanked us for our efforts. This sentiment was echoed by a similar French General Order signed by Canrobert. These and the actual capture of the position gave us some satisfaction, as we were less than one hundred yards from Russian artillery batteries. This meant we were now excellently placed to pour in fire on their main redoubts. To safeguard whoever was manning our new position, protecting walls were soon built on the approaches to it to allow replacement pickets and reinforcements to come and go.

The Russians, now under pressure from our nearness, attempted to retake the rifle pits. They were driven back but not before killing two more riflemen and wounding many more.

On the 26th November, Captain Fortune again sent for me asking if I would once more volunteer to accompany him into Sevastopol. Much as though there were many times when I wished I wasn't held in some regard by him, I felt obliged to accept, or had I volunteered anyway?

"We just take one rifleman," he said, "so it'll be only the four of us. Maybe a bit trickier this time as the Russkies are likely to be more on edge after the batterin' we've been givin' them. We'll also be joined by Major Rivers."

I said, "I'll volunteer Williams again. He's a miserable bleeder but he's reliable and did very well last time."

Later that same day, Major Rivers joined us and, under cover of darkness and the ever-present pall of smoke that hung over the town, we left our lines. As we moved forward our artillery began to shell the redoubts, which helped keep Russian heads down, as we passed unseen through their outlying pickets. One piece of shrapnel did rip Captain Fortune's borrowed Russian greatcoat sleeve to shreds and left the cuffs of his Rifle's tunic hanging down in thin strips.

After an hour's slow progress through piles of rubble and several dead bodies, and a slightly different route to the one we had taken previously, we found our way blocked by the heaped remains of a battered house. All around were smouldering pieces of timber. We edged left and forward but the way was barred by a building that although roofless proved still to be habitable.

Unfortunately, standing outside of the curtained doorway was a young officer, smoking and taking in the evening air; not that the fires burning all round would have made the air particularly pleasant.

We had stopped suddenly. His standing there barring our way had been a surprise but we had seen him only just in time; a second or two more and we would have blundered into him.

His body was framed by candlelight from inside the room.

If we took a shot at him it might be just heard even though the noise of artillery, soldiers moving around constantly and the crackling of burning timber should be enough to drown it out. But we were nearer than those other sounds and a single shot and the flash of powder as the Enfield was discharged might just be detected. If the man at the door had companions inside the room and then fell backwards into the room after being shot, it might have turned out to be very bad for us. If we did shoot him and rushed forward very quickly, would they still have time to stop us?

I drew Captain Fortune back a few paces.

"I reckon if I could crawl close enough before rushing him back into whoever else is in the room we might catch 'em off guard. I'd have to chance whether or not there are more behind the curtain. If there is, I might just be able to get them before they get me or before you, Williams and Major Rivers can get in to help."

During the time I had been whispering my plan to Mr. Fortune, I had been studying my opponent. He was a tall, good-looking, dark-haired and moustachioed officer. Not the usual heavily bearded Russian. Instead, he had a neatly trimmed rather thin one that could have been almost painted on above his upper lip. He had very piercing eyes, even from the distance I was from him, and I had that uneasy feeling that he knew exactly what I was planning to do. He was quite heavily built, but if I managed to charge at him and catch him in the right place, I could bowl him over.

"Right," agreed the captain, "give it a try. You'll have to take him by surprise, catch him just right and hopefully wind him or you'll be in trouble. Perhaps his companions may be in a different room. He'll be out of puff and won't be able to call out."

I hoped that this would prove to be true as I carefully laid my rifle to one side and prepared to creep forward.

"Finch," interrupted Major Rivers, "if you could just push him over but not kill him. He looks like an artilleryman from his uniform. We might learn something useful from him. So don't kill him straight away, there's a good fellow."

By now the man's cigar had been smoked over halfway down. I needed to go before he finished it and returned to his billet. We had to go past him as we could hear a lot of movement from back behind the way we had come. I removed anything that might make a noise by hitting rubble and began to ease myself forward, crawling as quietly as I could to within about six paces of him. He was standing, turned slightly to his left as I launched myself at him just as he was turning to go back inside.

I caught him just below the ribs. He grunted and almost folded in half as we tumbled into the room. I looked quickly around, taking in the almost bare room at a glance. It was quite small, illuminated by a lantern. It had probably been the reception area in this originally two-storey house. As I straightened up Major Rivers pushed our prisoner back and then covered him with his pistol. I noticed a large canvas sheet above our heads. Its four corners each had a length of rope tied to them, which were in turn attached to nails in each of the four corners of the room. The middle of the canvas, which had almost certainly been a sail from a ship, sagged.

The whole room had a damp plaster smell to it and in the lantern's light we could see flecks of plaster as they drifted down from the ceiling onto the canvas plaster catcher below and where the weight along one of it's sides had brought it down only chest high.

The room itself was sparsely furnished; there was a camp

bed, above which was a large and very colourful icon where the occupant's head would rest. A small table had cigars, papers, books and writing materials strewn across it.

While Williams took up station just inside the curtain door to keep watch, occasionally peering cautiously out, Major Rivers was pushing the still winded and rather red-faced Russian into a chair. He then, in French and from time to time in Russian, began to question our captive, who, from the somewhat slumped position in the seat, was struggling to regain some dignity. I thought it odd that educated Russians still seemed to prefer speaking French rather than their native language to their equals in society, though both languages were in use on this occasion. After a few minutes Rivers turned to Captain Fortune and me.

"This," he said, waving his revolver at the Russian, "is Lieutenant Count Lev Nikolayevich Tolstoi, who is part of the 3rd Light Battery of the 14th Artillery Brigade. He has not long arrived in town after being prompted to do something after the Russian defeat at Inkerman. Like us, he was surprised that our smaller force was successful against his countrymen. From the tone in his voice and what he is not saying he seems to have a poor view of those in high command. It appears too that soldiers in their army are not just poorly led but badly treated as well and, until changes are made, will continue to be slaughtered like cattle and not win, although their bravery is not in question. Oh, and he is rather peeved at being interrupted during his off-duty time. He spends enough of that as it is moving back and forth between here in the old town and his post on, I think he means, the Little Redan near the harbour. He also tells me that his servant, Andrey is due back at any time."

"No movement yet, sir," called Williams softly.

Captain Fortune remarked, "We'll just have to wait for the servant to come back. If we take any action now, the game's up."

By this he clearly meant that if the servant returned to the billet and found Tolstoi's dead body then the alarm would be raised.

Our prisoner, sensing the predicament he was in and the problem we had as well, spoke quickly to the Major.

"He says we already faced a difficult task as it is in getting back to our lines. So he is offering his parole not to raise the alarm for three hours after we leave if both he and his servant are not molested in any way."

Apparently his servant and the man's family had served the Tolstois on their estates long and loyally. Andrey was a simple, harmless man. His master, unlike the way we had seen some Russian officers treat their men, appeared to be quite concerned for this one.

Seconds later, Williams hissed a warning.

"Someone's coming."

He then moved to the side of the door, stood his rifle against the wall and drew his sword from its scabbard.

A small man, whistling cheerfully while backing through the curtained doorway, entered the room carrying a tray complete with bowls, bread and wine. Fortune grabbed him from behind, thrusting his left arm around the man's throat, while the pistol-filled palm of his right arm pushed the weapon hard against his temple. Williams deftly moved across and with one hand removed the tray.

Tolstoi, who had during this action remained covered by Major River's revolver, spoke quietly to the servant.

Andrey, slowly recovering from the captain's stranglehold, was gradually calming down. Colour was slowly returning to that part of his cheeks that remained above his beard.

The two officers were discussing what our next move should be. They could either leave the two Russians tied up, guarded by Williams, or, if the house had a cellar – and most did – they could be confined to it, again with Williams guarding them.

Neither officer seemed to consider killing our prisoners and sounded as though they would accept his parole. The Russian officer did give the strong impression that he could be trusted not to go against his word given to two fellow officers, albeit on different sides.

Grabbing a lantern I went off in search of the cellar. There was one, although it was half full of large pieces of collapsed ceilings from the floors above.

I moved a couple of doors, shifted some rubble and broken furniture and clambered back up the steps.

"It will do, sir," I said to Captain Fortune, "only one way in and out and that's the steps. I've set a couple of chairs for them and if we put that door across the top of the cellar and pile some of these in it," indicating some bricks, "it should be enough to stop them getting out too easily after the three hours is up after we leave."

The two Russians were marched out of the room and down the cellar steps.

Rivers spoke to Tolstoi again and then turned to the three of us.

"He thanks us for honouring his word. They will make no attempt to move after our departure for three hours."

"With luck," said Captain Fortune, "we should be back here in a couple of hours. Williams, if anyone does come into this house and moves towards the cellar you'll just have to protect yourself the best way you can. You could stay quiet and hope for the best or, try to get out and make your way back to our lines. Failing that, you could always throw yourself on their mercy."

"No bloody fear, sir," he said, "we've seen 'em bayonet wounded men and prisoners."

While they had been talking I had been eyeing the bread, soup and wine on the tray with some envy, but the two Russians were allowed to take their supper and a lighted candle to the depths below the house.

I would have to make do, as on many other occasions, with a hard biscuit. As their food disappeared below I stood by ready to place a door over the cellar entrance. As Captain Fortune returned from serving supper I heaved the door into place and put twenty or more bricks upon it. With a few words to Williams suggesting he sit at the top of the cellar with his rifle and canteen close to hand but without lighting a candle, I moved to the back of the house to join the two officers. We edged carefully through the familiar piles of rubble and burning wood. After about twenty minutes of cautious, sweaty progress we passed the House of Delights, as Captain Fortune called it, and stopped in our tracks as we reached the house where we had first encountered the Tatar spy. In front of it, bayoneted to a rough cross of blackened timbers, was our man. From the look on his face, the slash marks on his bare chest and the scorched and reddened arms and legs he had not died quickly or peacefully.

Nothing could be done for him. We couldn't even take him down. His wounds looked very recent and his torturers might not be too far away. We needed to look after ourselves. Major Rivers motioned us to retrace our steps and we turned considerably stunned and began to move away. Then, heading in our direction we caught sight of perhaps eight or ten Russian infantry and an officer with drawn sword. Perhaps they had managed to get the Tatar to talk and he had given details of when and where we would be.

"Down quickly," said Major Rivers, no doubt hoping like Captain Fortune and me that the enemy soldiers had not seen us.

Whether or not they had probably did not matter that much as they were moving directly towards us, and even if they did not see us they would certainly fall over us. Captain Fortune nodded at my rifle and then at me. I fired a shot and caught the officer high up on his chest. While I reloaded my two companions had rushed forward, firing their Colt revolvers at the temporarily stunned, confused and now leaderless Russians. About twenty seconds later, I shot another of the enemy from almost point-blank range. Then, fixing my sword, I charged at the survivors hoping that would be enough to persuade them to retreat. I crashed into one of them. As I withdrew my sword from below his ribs, I caught another full in the face with the butt of my rifle. This, and the revolver fire proved too much and they bolted.

Captain Fortune yelled, "Leave it, let's go," so we also turned and ran.

The Russians may have run off, but from somewhere there came the sound of shot and the hissing of musket balls all around us. We continued to run but whoever had fired must have lost any enthusiasm they had to pursue us.

Two or more minutes passed and we stopped to take shelter and catch our breath behind a wall. With chests heaving from our exertions we looked back the way we had bolted but could not see anyone following. I removed my sword and reloaded the Minié and pointed it back down the way we had come, just in case.

We stood up, rolled over another wall and set off for the house where we had left Williams.

"You two go on," suggested Captain Fortune, "I'll go and fetch Williams."

"Best if Sergeant Finch does that," said Major Rivers.

My company commander looked doubtful, but I said that I would fetch Williams and get us both back. Captain Fortune still looked a little uneasy at this for some reason but, urged by Rivers, was forced to realise that that was the obvious thing to do. I was, after all, only a sergeant.

As the two officers moved off toward the Russian front lines I turned towards the house where we had left the rifleman guarding the two Russians.

I had reloaded, but if I blundered into any Russians I would have a problem. One shot and a few jabs with the sword might not reduce the odds by very much. So I kept my sword in its scabbard, which was what we normally did when skirmishing, and made up my mind to move as slowly and as cautiously as I could in an effort to avoid the enemy, difficult in a town filled with soldiers and under siege but I had little choice. Step by step with my back easing along walls of varying sizes caused by our artillery, I reached the house with its curtained door. I pulled the curtain back, the candles we had left burning were beginning to splutter. My ears strained for any unusual noise, difficult because of the customary shell and musket fire. Nothing came from the depths just that eerie hush. Was Williams all right?

Calling "Rifles" every few paces, I moved towards the cellar. A sword point touched my right shoulder and in the light of that partly shuttered lantern he must have exchanged for a candle, I saw the scowling face of rifleman Williams.

***

"About bloody time, sarge," was his greeting, "get there all right?" he added.

"We ran into some trouble," I said, and quickly relayed the events of the last hour or two.

"What about his nibs and the servant?" he asked, jerking a thumb towards the barricaded cellar. "Do we croak 'em?"

"No, Mr. Fortune gave his word. I'll just move the door and tell them we're going. They may or may not give us the three hours but with the way things have gone I don't think that it matters too much either way. I'll speak to them and stick the door and bricks back. That should keep them busy at least for a few hours anyway, while they burrow their way out."

With that I eased some bricks off the door and managed to move it to one side. In my poor French, I called into the void, "Nous quittons. Trois heures."

A voice from below answered, "Merci, monsieur. Bonne chance."

Williams, in the light of the lantern, looked very impressed. I replaced the door and, adding a few large chunks of masonry to the bricks, stepped back, grabbed my rifle and moved back towards the curtain door that led to the outside.

"I didn't know that you could speak French, sarge," he said.

"I don't. Just picked up a few words here and there on my visits to their camp. It's better than my Russian. Talking of them we'll have to be really careful going back. A dead spy, a Russian patrol, two of our officers blundering their way back through their lines and the two down the cellar. The Russians could be waiting for us just to round off a perfect day."

So we left the house even more cautiously in our borrowed, dirty, buff-coloured greatcoats with their white crossbelts, pushed high up to our chins and hoped that the dark forage caps with their yellow bands and figure 3 would get us through to our lines. When we had started from our side of the Heights, Major Rivers on joining us had identified the captured uniforms as belonging to the Dneprovski Regiment of Grenadiers. They had left Balaklava in something of a hurry without much of their personal kit and equipment when our artillery had shelled the town. The regiment though, was still in and around Sevastopol he had said, and so we hoped our disguise would get us in and out of the town. It seemed to take an age before we reached the Barrack Battery and that spot in the Russian defensive line, which up to now had been poorly manned. From there we skirted the Great Redan and, taking great breaths, removed our borrowed clothes, which we threw behind some rocks and prepared to run across the open ground by the Quarries. Soon we were being challenged by our forward pickets.

About thirty minutes later I was reporting to Captain Fortune that we had left our prisoners alive and well and our passage back through the Russian lines had been without incident. He looked really pleased that we had both returned safely.

"Well done to you both. Good show," he said, slapping Williams on the back.

As we walked back in the direction of our own billets, I said, "You've done a damn good job. If anyone deserves a medal in this freezing hole, you do."

He looked at me. What was almost a smile played across his lips, albeit very briefly. He then said in a very subdued way, "Fine, sarge, but instead of a medal give me a ticket home."

We reached his cold, draughty billet and I moved on to mine, tired but satisfied that we had done our work well and surprised that I had almost seen a different side to the usually gloomy Williams.

It also occurred to me that up to then I hadn't really taken in how miserable the weather had become.

9

Now it was back to days of little food, little or no wood for our fires and the prospects of an increasingly bitterly cold December and January. The Russians were also still an ever-present threat and no doubt would still be making efforts to get past our pickets and cause as much confusion as they could. It was also more than likely that as a special rifle battalion we would be expected to provide cover for the engineers as they constructed more gun pits, and for the artillery as they fired their guns into Sevastopol.

Sometime in the spring, we would also be keeping enemy gunners heads down as some one would at long last be giving the order to finally storm the redoubts and take the town.

November's icy grip merged into an even colder December. Many men's feet were either swollen or numb with frostbite. Too often they were forced to cut off the heels of shoes so suffering feet could be eased inside them. The cries of men in pain could often be heard as I did the rounds of the pickets.

Although there had been the occasional day that was bright and even sunny, though certainly not warm, the weather was really bad.

On 2nd December, a company of riflemen marched down to the pits to relieve the 50th Regiment but found them in retreat. Somehow the Russians had surprised them. Perhaps the bitter cold had dulled the senses of the defenders.

***

Angry at this, our officer in charge of the relief column ordered swords to be fixed and we charged in among them and in a matter of about twenty minutes we had taken it back and sent the enemy off in confusion.

Roads in the winter were almost impassable and were one of the reasons why supplies were not reaching us. I decided to go down to Balaklava myself and if needs be buy some supplies. I understood that biscuits, bread, cheese and meats could be easily obtained for the right price. As I picked my way down to the town – it was a Thursday, 7th December – I came across two wagons, each drawn by six horses lumbering with some difficulty up the steep track. Loaded, not with much needed food, but coils of wire, batteries, a collection of odd looking instruments and what I took to be some kind of plough. As I looked into the wagons moving at less than walking pace, my first thought was what a waste of good wagon space. Puzzled and curious in equal measure I engaged two sappers of the Field Electric Telegraph in conversation. They said the plough-looking machine was indeed a plough but a special one to dig a trench for laying wire. They would soon be burying enough wire so that messages could be sent from the Monastery of St George at Balaklava to our siege lines at Sevastopol. It would then link up with all the Divisions on the Heights. Soon, they said, messages would be sent from our positions all across the Black Sea to Varna. I marvelled at this 'telegraph' only wishing it could do the same for food and other supplies. It should though send messages requesting supplies very quickly. It was just in the delivery that seemed to create the problem.

Leaving them to wend their slow progress across the Heights I continued on my way down towards Balaklava Harbour. Suddenly, I was challenged by an invisible voice,

"Who goes there?" it demanded.

"Friend, Sergeant John Finch, 1st Battalion, Rifle Brigade," I called back in the general direction of the voice.

"Advance, sergeant."

At this, I saw a Royal Marines Artilleryman gradually rise and by stages come into view. I saw first his black felt shako with the Corps badge on the front and white tuft on its top. Then came his blue, double-breasted coatee with shiny brass buttons, then whitish-gloved hands and arms holding a Minié carbine and finally, as he came almost into full view, blue trousers.

Since my last foray into the town, the Royal Marines had evidently been hard at work. Their guns, 24 and 32-pounders by the look of them, now protected the harbour from the heights above, now called the Marine Heights. Some of their guns, as well as those of the Royal Artillery, also pointed across the Balaklava Valley towards the Causeway Heights.

Across the Vorontsov Road and to the left and right of Kodoikoi they had been constructing defensive lines and on the left fringes of their lines above Balaklava where an attack had occurred earlier. And where future assaults against the town, or a flanking movement and attack on our lines before Sevastopol might happen, they had prepared a very impressive and formidable abbatis with lengths of sharpened timbers at the heart of it.

This also went someway to explaining what had happened to much of what we could have used as fuel.

On part of the gorge that ran up from Balaklava, and just to the right of where my challenger had been standing, a large, heavy-looking gate barred the rut-strewn path that passed for the road, facing outwards from the town.

I watched as a small party of Marines climbed the highest point of their defences and began to signal using semaphore-arms across the valley towards the siege lines; quick, silent and effective, though not much use when mist hangs over the valley. This seemed to occur often, but then messengers could be sent should the enemy try a surprise attack. Always hoping that in a mist they could be seen before they mounted an attack.

The Marines had been able to signal for reinforcements when, in early October, Russian prisoners had told them that their Tatar spies were planning on firing English stores in Balaklava itself. The Russian plan then had been to bring confusion to the allied rear while at the same time they would begin an attack at the Chernaya River. It seemed that the Tatars could be bought by both sides.

Later, on 18th October, all Marines had stood to arms beside their artillery pieces in case, as was suspected, the enemy was about to attack in force. When they did eventually move on allied positions a week later they had managed to disperse the Turks.

The Marines were delayed by a heavy mist, but eventually gave artillery support as the enemy had turned against the Highlanders, and the Light Brigade had made that spectacular but doomed charge against those Russian guns.

As I wandered back from Balaklava with my knapsack crammed with a few necessities, I looked down and across towards Inkerman. I could still see the remains of men who had only been buried in very shallow graves after the battle that had taken place nearby. There was though, the rather more comforting sight of the two redoubts and an artillery battery close at hand watching for that possible approach by the Russians.

The weather continued to be bad. By the 16th December the ground was covered in snow. While we shivered in holes covered by canvas and thin blankets, wet and hungry, dragging everything we needed up from Balaklava, we also continued to do a twelve-hour duty in the trenches.

Five days later the Russians attacked the French on our left and our positions at Green Hill, but were pushed back after hard fighting.

The 23rd and 24th December was particularly cold with sleet and rain.

While shivering in my rain-soaked 'tent' my thoughts turned to home and of a particular incident by the river. I had, I think, been summoned from my job in Winchester to see my father who had been taken ill earlier in the day. He had collapsed in the bakery where he had been helping out. He looked very ill when I saw him, but protested over what he called a fuss about nothing. By the evening he pronounced himself well enough for work.

I had decided not to return to Winchester the next day, but give it – the Wednesday – over to idleness.

Thinking about what happened later that day generally raised more than my spirits.

In the middle of that warm, late spring morning during that time I was giving serious thought to what I should do with my life beyond the butcher's shop, I wandered along the riverbank where my poaching career had been so short-lived. For several years that unsatisfied and unsettled feeling had never been too far away. Captain, or as he was then Lieutenant Fortune had been as good as his word. Small parcels of books had been left outside my cottage door. A little note was usually attached with words such as, '*For Master Jack Finch, find a use for these.*'

In some ways these had helped stir that vein of discontent that had long been developing. I found stories of adventure and of strange lands. As I looked about my freezing billet in the Crimea I thought that I couldn't be in much more of a stranger place than that. It was not quite what I had dreamed about a few years before. Books though, had opened up a wider world so much different to the butcher's shop in Winchester that I had temporarily on that Wednesday escaped from, and far removed from the cottage in the village of Lower Durford in Hampshire.

***

The river where I had so often escaped to, dropped about three feet, passing over rocks which, when the river was high after heavy rain formed a frothing waterfall that dropped into the lower section of the river, and on to join the River Test and then to the sea. The pond was fringed around half of its circumference by chest-high bushes and beyond them, and forming shade from the sun from about ten in the morning to around three in the afternoon, was a stand of sycamore trees.

I eased myself down to just in front of the hawthorn, stretched out and looked deeply into the pond. The river was in full spate after the heavy spring showers of recent days had drained off the hills beyond and the fields further upstream. By the time it reached the rocky threshhold above the pond it was clear and sparkled in the sun's rays. Little rainbows played just above and below the waterfall.

Nearby, according to what the villagers had told the local boys, there had been a monastery, Durford Priory, but the buildings were long gone since the days of King Henry. Many of the stones had been taken to build the Hall as well as farms and cottages scattered all around. The Fortunes' ancestors had apparently gained more land from King Henry's destruction of the monasteries adding to what earlier kings had given them long before.

The monks had probably been the first to realise the benefits of the river and had deepened this tributary of the Test. They were the first to build a mill and enlarge the pond.

So flour from the mill to bake their bread, and fish from the pond provided much of what they needed for Fridays, Lent and the other holy days. Other buildings followed over time, including a small brewery and a bakery.

As I rested there, hands behind my head, I struggled to focus on the scene in front of me as the warmth of the day and the restful sound of water both combined to make my eyelids droop. Then odd noises broke the spell of sleepy daydreaming; excited voices and giggling were heading in my direction. My dozing, lulled by the birds nesting in the trees behind me, brought my lapses into adventures I longed to have to a sudden stop. I sat up and leaned forward cautiously. Approaching my resting-place in a very leisurely way was a small group of girls just a year or two older than me. They were only about sixty yards away when I decided I must do something. I moved backward behind the bushes and slunk off into the trees. Luckily for me they were too busy to notice my presence. New growth on the hawthorn had given me excellent cover.

I would often reflect much later, while skirmishing in my dark rifle green uniform, on the question why the English Army insisted on most of its soldiers marching into battle in bright red tunics. A perfect target, while we riflemen were very often just able to merge into the background.

From the bushes I moved into the trees and above a part of the pond that was visible from behind a tree trunk. I then thought that I should go and leave them to their own entertainment and return home.

***

My attention was taken up by the movements of one of this small company. I knew the person, or rather, I had seen her a few times at church or near the Hall. She was Lady Sophie Fortune, one of the younger sisters of James Fortune.

Within a few moments, as she hung her drawers, along with the rest of her clothes carefully on a nearby bush she was completely naked. I numbered sisters among my family and was aware of their strange garments and had unintentionally glimpsed them washing at the pump but had seen nothing like the clothes or the bare form that now stood ankle deep in the shallows of the pond not too far from where I stood. My storybooks had enchanted me and I had often been carried away on flights of fancy as I had grown up, but nothing compared with this new, enchanting sight that I was now breathlessly beholding. Her flame-red hair, now unpinned, cascaded down the soft curve of that bare back. Her milk-white skin seemed to glisten in that same sunshine that had also warmed my own, if browner skin. Her arms were long and slender though folded in a half-hearted attempt at modesty. She stood with legs together. Above the crease made by her slim thighs was a thicket of soft, downy looking hair that in the sunlight was a mottled, light brown, flecked with gold colour that formed a perfect 'V'.

I was held like a moth in a candle flame as I watched her turn and step further into the water. Seconds later she turned back, standing up to her waist, shivering slightly. She held out her arms to her friends, beseeching them to join her in the pond. As she did so I caught sight of her erect, pinky-tan-coloured nipples, delicately poised on small, but firm-looking breasts that pointed directly towards the trees where I stood skulking.

Her teeth were chattering as she called out, "Oh, do come in. It really isn't that bad once you're in."

Lady Sophie's companions appeared less anxious to expose themselves, though several did begin the lengthy process of unbuttoning various items of clothing. This, while I rather reluctantly but fearing discovery, began to slink away. I felt a little ashamed but at the same time more than thrilled by what I had just seen. I felt sure she had, or would have, many admirers and suitors. As I crept away I added myself if rather forlornly to that list of admirers.

I had known for years that the pond was a favourite spot for bathing among the young gentlemen of James Fortune's acquaintance, but this had been something different and I did return a number of times hoping to see the same again as that vision of Lady Sophie. It did though remain with me and warm and comfort me on many a long night in the years to come.

Sadly, this beautiful girl that I could only admire from afar, was married off by her father not long after her dip in the pond, to a wealthy, if sour-faced lord. She died along with her infant at about the same time that I was marching across Cape Colony in pursuit of Moshesh, the king of the Xhosas.

I had heard the news from Lieutenant Fortune himself. For some reason he seemed to have sought me out deliberately and in that rather matter of fact way of his, had mentioned her passing during some task or other that involved rounding up tribesmen who had been stealing cattle. He did though appear to sound better for having shared this sad news with me.

***

After telling me, he moved away then half-turned and fixed me with a long, thoughtful look that made me feel very uneasy. I had been caught off-guard when he had told me and had only managed to mumble a few words saying how sorry I was at this information. I still remained puzzled as to why he had singled me out, a mere corporal at the time, but spear-throwing natives distracted me from further consideration of the puzzle.

Back in the Crimea, there was a continuing shortage of most things, including fuel. Each man was entitled to a regular supply in order to cook what was supposed to be our daily food allowance. All our supplies had to be hauled up from Balaklava, so my visits to the French camp only aggravated our knowing how much worse off we were than our allies. Their supply base at Kamiesh continued to regularly send wagon trains bursting with supplies to their siege lines. This, while our stores were often just left aboard ships to await unloading and then, once ashore, the slow plod up to our camps. The French were better able to unload, warehouse and then transport it. The French supply base was so much easier to reach. On some pretext or other I had found myself looking along the Kamiesh harbour front with warehouses stacked to the roofs. Newly butchered meat could be in the French camp in a few hours. Not so us. From Balaklava the ground rose quite sharply. The seven or so miles to our camp was marked by deep ruts in a road that was little better than rough tracks. Horses, mules and men faced a muscle-testing plod as they hauled and struggled with all manner of foods up that incline.

***

A shortage of fresh vegetables had also led to an outbreak of scurvy in our battalion. By the time much of it had been brought ashore it was found to be unfit to eat.

As well as eating better food regularly our allies seemed more confident and more easily able to cope with the local terrain than many English regiments. Captain Fortune said that this was probably down to what they had learned while campaigning in Algeria, particularly the regiment of Zouaves.

Only very slowly, and I was told rather reluctantly at that, did our Commissariat begin to adopt French methods for the distribution of meats and in the setting up of an English style of mobile canteens.

Food shortages and a lack of medical services meant that the number of soldiers in our whole army was calculated at only around 10,000 by the middle of December who could be considered fit enough for duty. Going around our camp at this time was the rumour that surgeons did have a method by which they could put a badly injured man to sleep during an amputation or other dangerous treatment. Yet in spite of this our surgeons seemed to prefer to operate on patients who remained awake. If the man cried out in pain then he was still alive and according to their reasoning more likely to survive the ordeal.

10

The year 1855 began just as the old year had ended, cold and miserable. Grumbling among the men criticising the army commanders was even spreading to officers in my own regiment, as nothing was being achieved other than rising numbers being added daily to those joining the sick-list. By the 4th January, the snow was deep and conditions so bad that a party of riflemen sent to collect and haul supplies from Balaklava had to abandon the attempt.

The black-bearded Colonel Windham rode into our camp the next day and made a general enquiry into how we were faring. He did look very concerned when I overheard a man from the 63rd saying that out of his company only about half of them were capable of carrying out their duties in the trenches. Dysentery was widespread, men were still wet and hungry. Fuel was almost non-existent. The Colonel looked very grave on being told this and said he would try and push for supplies; food, fuel, shelter and boots being the most urgently required, to be brought up. Life for those doing a watch in the trenches was particularly difficult.

On 12th January, the Russians attacked, causing a lot of confusion among the men suffering already from the cold and snow. The enemy sortie came as quite a surprise. There were a few casualties, but many more missing believed captured by the enemy.

Two days later we scrabbled about in the snow desperately looking for roots or anything else that we could use as fuel. How long could we continue in this condition? If the Russians were able to gather their forces and mount an attack they might just be able to sweep us off the Heights. It was hoped that the men who had been captured would keep quiet about how desperate things generally and morale particularly was, in the English camp. Yet one look at the men they had seized who looked little better than scarecrows would give them all the intelligence they needed to tell them how we were all faring.

On 24th January, we received a new draft of thirty-two men to replace casualties from both action and sickness. The new men looked around our camp in some amazement at the ragged figures. They saw men wrapped in pieces of blanket, with lengths of the same material tied around their feet, slapping their arms across their bodies and stamping their feet in a desperate effort to keep out the cold, or just shuffling their feet in a chilled trance.

And so it continued. We were fighting the bitter Russian weather all day, every day and most evenings there was an exchange of musket and rifle fire to contend with as well as grape and shell.

Over those days odd pieces of hut began to arrive. Around Sunday the 4th February we received some oranges and tea. Perhaps this was the first signs of that much needed improvement after all.

It could though, just be a false dawn as we could see the Russians giving their full attention to building up their defences on and around the low hill just in front of the Malakoff, called the Mamelon.

***

As we could see them clearly, we fired into their midst from time to time. What was causing us additional concern were the numbers of men involved; far more than could normally and comfortably be accommodated in their gun pits. It was suggested by one of our officers that these extra men were helping to dig underground defences. The spoil from their tunnelling was being taken out under cover of darkness and was probably being used to strengthen the walls of the redoubt.

Earlier, back in January, they had after all exploded a large quantity of powder in a trench out from the Malakoff. Both the Russians and the French had spent a lot of time cutting tunnels towards each other's lines. Artillery fire accompanied both sets of tunnel explosions as they attempted to stop the other side from breaking into each other's saps. It did provide us with a spectacular display and a reminder of what we were enduring the bitterest of winters for, the capture of Sevastopol. Rather surprisingly, it seemed to take the French by surprise.

On Saturday, 17th February and to everyone's surprise we heard that the Russians had launched an attack against the Turks at Evpatoria. This was a town on the northern coast of Kalamita Bay, not far from where we had landed. Was that only about six months ago? But what were the Russians up to? Did they think that the Turks were about to send reinforcements for that long-awaited move against Sevastopol? Or, was this the first step in the Russians opening up that part of the Crimea for their extra forces to help out their besieged countrymen in that town?

Would our army commanders order us to leave our lines at Sevastopol and cut off a possible enemy supply line from the Russian mainland through Perekop?

On 20th February we were told at our frosty morning parade that Sir Colin Campbell would be leading his Highland brigade at the same time as a French force to attack the Russians.

"Be extra vigilant, men," we were ordered, "as the enemy may try and use this joint attack to sneak in and surprise us."

As an added precaution against a possible assault, three companies of riflemen were sent forward to strengthen our picket lines.

The following day a Russian force was engaged, but most of

them managed to escape without suffering too many casualties. The weather was blamed for our side not being able to inflict greater damage on the enemy.

On 23rd the French mounted an attack against the Mamelon but it was pushed back with heavy losses.

The next day, when the battalion paraded, we were told we were to be issued with a new rifle during the day. So later we exchanged the Minié for the Enfield. Although most riflemen had found it to be quite a good weapon and certainly an improvement on the Brunswick, the Minié had not been popular with everyone. During the days that followed we adapted to the new long weapon. It was of a slightly smaller calibre than the Minié, but just as powerful and certainly more accurate. It also seemed to allow us to load it very quickly and almost without having to think about it. Cartridges were issued in a paper packet tied with string.

The top of the cartridge was opened with the teeth and the charge of powder inside it tipped down the barrel. The bullet is then reversed and rammed down the barrel to sit directly on the powder charge. The hammer is pulled to half cock, a percussion cap placed on the nipple that will be struck by the hammer and pushed firmly down using the thumb. Then the hammer is pulled to full cock ready for firing. Most of us after some practise could load and fire three times to the minute. Even rifleman Williams seemed pleased with how the rifle performed, though he had made quite a sensible comment when I had handed him his new weapon.

"Third rifle in about six months. Let's hope this one's been tested in a real war and with a sword fixed to it and not just fired in the butts."

There were a few early problems. The bands holding the barrel in place caught in the cloth of our uniforms. They were later replaced with solid barrel bands that had countersunk screws. The bayonet, or sword, still triangular in section, had a curved blade and some of us found it very difficult to withdraw. It was, however, still attached using the same method as the sword we had used with the Minié with a spring catch, which gripped a collar on the sword itself. The curved end of the hammer also seemed rather too prone to breaking.

Over the course of the next few weeks some of the allied forces were deployed north to Evpatoria. There they came across many Tatars living in poverty, having run away from what they had feared might be Russian retribution for their enthusiastic welcoming of the allies the previous September.

***

It seemed to the allies that if they landed reinforcements around Cape Tarakan then they could once and for all bottle up all Russian forces in the Crimea. We could then if required, march north of Sevastopol and trap them between us, and our army at the Cape. It was also believed, certainly hoped, that the Tatars would be likely to join forces with the allies and so bring an early end to this Russian war.

Once again allied energies returned to the business of besieging Sevastopol. We, the other ranks, were forming the strong opinion that hesitancy was once more setting in the allied commanders minds, and they were still disagreeing how and what form the assault on the town should take. The enemy, on the other hand seemed more resolute and launched a night attack on the 7th Fusiliers, the 90th Light Infantry and the 97th of the Light Division causing considerable confusion and many casualties. By the time messages had reached us, the enemy had drifted back to Sevastopol leaving behind about the same number as our side, one hundred dead and wounded. If they had intended to unsettle our army, they had been quite successful. What else had the Russians been planning and how much had they boosted their defensive lines? During late

March, I was once again asked by Captain Fortune to volunteer.

"This time, Finchy, we're escortin' a Royal Sappers and Miners officer to get a bird's eye view of their defences."

We knew that the Malakoff was heavily fortified and that the other bastion will be difficult to take as well.

***

Whatever the Russians had been up to, the task of capturing the town would now be even harder. Had they mined their redoubts as well as building up the walls that we would have to climb before dropping down into the gunpits themselves? If we did manage to capture the Great Redan would we find ourselves being blown sky high just as they had detonated their forward trenches out from the Malakoff? Their defences had certainly improved in quality from wickerwork, fascines and gabons. Now their bastions were reinforced by adding casements. These were heavily protected gun emplacements excavated to a depth of several yards and then covered with heavy ships' timbers and earthworks.

As before, I met up with my two travelling companions, Captain Fortune and Captain Bantock of the Royal Sappers and Miners. My company commander was trying on a Russian greatcoat over his uniform. As on the previous occasions, he carried a Colt revolver in a holster and an Enfield.

"Don't worry, Finchy, bin practisin' with it," he grinned.

His fellow officer was also armed with a revolver, an Adams, and was also dressed in a greatcoat and carried a carbine and a white belt, complete with a sword bayonet in its scabbard that he had borrowed from one of the men in his company. Once again, we hoped to pass as Russian infantrymen.

We waited until the early hours of the 21st March and crept towards the Russian lines, crossing them at that weak spot that the Russians had yet to strengthen.

***

Though, with guns bristling from almost every angle on the Garden and Barrack Batteries, any mass attack by the English and French there would face the withering artillery fire not only from these two positions, but the Great Redan and the Malakoff as well.

It had been decided, not by me, that we were to head for the House of Delights. But more encouragingly, I was then told by Captain Fortune that we were to meet up with, in his words, an old friend, Major Rivers. Unlike the three of us he was a Russian speaker and had gone on ahead to rendezvous with one of his spy contacts, another Tatar. His task was to find us a suitable hiding place from where, he, Rivers, and Captain Bantock could overlook the Great Redan and Malakoff.

We reached the house, met up with the spy and the Major and moved north-east, past the southern end of the Man of War Harbour and to a corner of what seemed to be a barrack block. My expression in the gloom must have looked sufficiently worried to prompt Major Rivers to exclaim, "Don't worry, we should be quite safe. It was, until our artillery started to paste it, a naval barracks. They've all moved out of this particular part of it as it looks as though it might just collapse at any moment. We should have an excellent view from here."

His words, though well meant, didn't do much to console me, especially the 'it might just collapse at any moment', but I couldn't really do much about that.

As dawn filtered through the all too murky aspect of a town under siege we had breakfast, cold but at least it was food.

Captain Bantock and Major Rivers crept to a nearby window opening and drew sketchbooks from inside their pouches. Both men began to draw with enthusiasm. The one looking at the Russian gunpits from the point of view of silencing their offensive potential, the other looking at where, if he were planting mines for the defence of the bastions, he would put them.

The spy once again had just drifted away. Hopefully he would not meet with the same fate as the other Tatar had met, or give us away. I further hoped that the agitated look he had while he was with us was down to a natural fear, rather than the anticipation of our being rounded up if he had been in league with the Russians.

The sapper officer casually mentioned, with some envy I think, that the fortifications seemed well made and were built especially to soak up a lot of punishment from our artillery. That large amount of soil they had employed in front of their positions would serve to just deaden the full effects of shells falling on it. He also pointed out that the Russian guns were situated low in their pits, under the earthworks. This would give our sharpshooters in the rifle pits a problem in being able to hit a clearly defined target. Up until recently the guns had rested quite high up in the bastion. Now when the gunners tended their guns they offered only very fleeting glimpses of their upper bodies and heads for us to shoot at. Captain Bantock had also commented that the earthworks also seemed to contain many bodies.

With that cheery information he added, "I'm just going to try and get a little closer. You wait here. I'll be back soon."

He then moved off, followed rather reluctantly by the major who evidently did not want to be left out of a chance of getting a better view.

While we waited on their return, Captain Fortune turned to me and in a very quiet, confidential tone said, "You know, Jack, you would make a very fine officer. A lot better than many of 'em in this army."

At this I replied with a great deal of surprise in my voice, "No, sir. I come from the wrong side of the estate, as you know. I couldn't afford it and can you really see me in your mess back home, surrounded by gold and silver plate, chatting to 'Sir this' or 'Lord that' with my best broad 'ampshire?"

"Oh, you wouldn't need to buy a commission, which we both know is the easy way in. Just 'cos a fellow has a few thousand and buys himself a rank, don't mean he'll be any good. And, it's not how you say it that matters but what you do that commands respect in the men."

"No," I said. "I'll stick to what I know, sir, but I appreciate your confidence in me."

I was also only too aware of several examples in this present campaign of sergeants and others who had gone on to be promoted without having to pay for the privilege.

I also knew of one man who had not been able to make the move, or mix well in the officer class and had blown his brains out.

Captain Fortune still seemed determined to have the final say.

"No, Jack, it's not just that you have shown great promise, private to sergeant in just a few years. The colonel is well aware of your leadership qualities and will give you his support. One of the reasons why we're here again in this God-forsaken place," waving his arm in a broad sweep, "is because of your loyalty to the regiment, to the men in your company and to me. All this has not gone unnoticed. You know your men and when you need to praise or give them a tongue-lashing. As you know, the Brigade encourages its riflemen to act independently. That seems to come easily and naturally to you. Perhaps lurkin' around ponds, rivers and libraries helped."

At that he chuckled to himself and then continued in a more serious tone, "There's something else. Another reason that should have probably been mentioned to you years ago, but you know what it's like livin' where we do."

I took that to mean how villagers were given to gossiping about anything, but just as it looked as though he was going to continue and tell me the reason, the two officers returned from their advanced sketching mission. I was partly relieved at their 'intrusion' following Captain Fortune's very flattering character assessment, but pleased it had been given in the gloom of our hiding place. All that praise was making my face flush with embarrassment.

***

I was, however, a little worried about what it could be that I should have been told years before. Then I returned my full attention to our situation and a brief chill of fear swept over me. We were after all surrounded by our enemies.

"It's an incredible piece of work," enthused Captain Bantock. "They've really strengthened the redoubts. By Jove, it's going to be a heck of a job getting past those defences. There are though, no obvious signs that the floor of the Great Redan has been mined."

"The sooner we get in there the better," added Major Rivers.

This news was worrying, particularly for those like me, who might very well find themselves in the first assault wave.

We spent the rest of a thankfully uneventful day just resting and eating our adequate if bland rations.

"Time to go," said Mr. Fortune.

As we returned to our lines on the night of the 22nd / 23rd March, we passed crouching figures occasionally caught in the eerie light thrown up by the flash from artillery pieces. A large force of Russian infantry were heading to the left and right of the Mamelon and Redan positions towards the French Right. We joined the right wing of this advance, as this would take us close to the Quarries. The sound of a drum roll added to the noise of the guns firing from behind us and those opening up in front of us. We continued to move forward in with the Russian advance. Captain Fortune was leading, then Major Rivers, followed by Captain Bantock with me in the rear. Shells were whistling uncomfortably close to us.

***

Three of us flung ourselves instinctively down as nearby Russians were caught by grapeshot. Captain Bantock had not been quick enough. One of our own shells caught him high in the ribs and reduced his chest to a bloody pulp. He was killed instantly. The drawings he had so carefully executed gone with him. We could do nothing but continue to move forward along with the enemy force as our unwitting escort. The noise of our boots and the scraping of our rifles as we ran, crouched and then crawled over the rocky ground with the Russians all around us adding a particular sound and excitement to the confused din of battle.

Then we saw the French, with bayonets fixed, advancing to engage the Russians and us as well. Taking our lead from Captain Fortune and just before the two forces crashed into each other, we moved right and then ran forward, reaching an advanced picket of men from our own lines who were there to check which direction the Russian force was going. By now the French and the Russians were at each other. The familiar crack of rifle shots, the thud of rifle butts as contact was made with bone and the screams of men in pain.

The Russians were slowly but surely being pushed back, but were not finished yet. Some had even reached the spot where we had met up with the pickets. Their reinforcements were also pouring out of the Malakoff and were spreading out left and right, but not without some difficulty. They were having to drop from the parapets of their defensive positions before they could properly engage the French and so add their weight to the original attacking force.

The Russians were then engaging our lines as well as the French and our soldiers in their advanced positions were having to fall back. Then a force of Zouaves, English infantry and a company of riflemen arrived and charged into the advancing enemy, who had been badly mauled by those French bayonets.

The Russians began to retreat and were soon in full, confused and fearful flight, especially as shells from both sides were soon whining overhead. The three of us leaning against the walls of a battery of mortars, clapped and cheered enthusiastically as a second wave of allied infantry rushed past us and joined the fray. Thirty minutes later, bugles sounded and our men returned to their positions.

As dawn broke, a scene of carnage met our gaze. Hundreds of Russian bodies littered the ground with a lesser number of allied casualties. An hour later a truce was arranged. For the two hours that followed, men scurried back and forth retrieving corpses and assisting wounded men to the field hospitals.

There was during this interlude an unusual sight. Red and blue-coated English and French were standing idly talking or gesturing with a comic range of arm signals, with grey and dark uniformed Russians. Men who just a few hours before had been intent on shooting, bayoneting or clubbing each other into oblivion, were now standing in that field of death, sharing tobacco, rum and casually smoking. When the two hour truce had finally come to an end, enemies shook hands and, with an occasional glance over their shoulders just in case, began to walk back to their own lines.

Contact similar to this between soldiers of opposite pickets had happened before, but was generally frowned on by officers. But it had been officers on this occasion who had made that first contact! One of my regular duties as a company sergeant was to check on the alertness of pickets guarding against a sudden attack. On one occasion back in December I had come across one of our sentries sharing his tobacco with a Russian soldier. As I had challenged our rifleman, the enemy soldier melted into the dark embrace of the night towards his own lines. I need not repeat the five minutes worth of words that followed. I think it most unlikely that he would ever do that again in a hurry. Later, I suggested to my company commander that while the cold of winter continued, pickets should be paired or the distance between each one reduced.

The daily routine of shells crashing around us, the hiss and whine of bullets, the buzzing of grapeshot, the shower of smaller shells leaving their own trails that lit up the night sky, continued. So used had men become to this that most of them just kept low and continued playing cards, ate the rations, repaired equipment and did similar tasks. Death still managed to seek out the unwary. But of all the weapons that the enemy flung at us the one that did cause men to pause as they carried out their duties was the mortar shell. Huge balls, some two feet across were thrown high in the air. Their fuse leaving a fiery trail as up they rose and then followed a curving path as it plunged with gathering speed until it reached its target.

It then exploded, throwing out metal splinters far and wide that inflicted horrific injuries as they tore through cloth and flesh. If one came my way the only hope was to fling myself to the ground and just hope for the best. I had seen men blown to pieces by mortars!

A few days after our return, I went in search of the captain hoping to continue that mysterious conversation we had in Sevastopol but was told he had gone down to Balaklava on horseback. I wandered back to my billet and on the way looked across at the Russian defences. That advanced protection to the Malakoff seemed to have been secured and to have been completed. I thought they had done very well to have achieved this under an almost daily bombardment during most of February and into the present month of March by the French. Attempts by our ally to interrupt their working parties by sending out infantry had generally been a failure. Most nights the Russians had sent out their own men against French lines. While this had been occurring the Russians had been busy building. It had also been suggested by Captain Bantock that the shelling by the French had actually helped the Russians. It gave them deep holes for the Russian working parties to hide in and from where their earthworks seemed to spring from. That seemed to be the case with the Mamelon. It had been bad enough early on, but shelling had helped turn it into an even more formidable position. This forward-bastion on a rocky hill was designed to provide advanced protection to the Malakoff, as well as adding more firepower from its flanks against any approach from the French right towards the Malakoff.

This, from the Quarries towards the Great Redan was likely to be where we would be attacking from. While we attacked the Redan the French left would probably also launch an attack against the Garden and Barrack Batteries. Our only hope would be to keep the Russians fully occupied with an attack across a wide part of their lines.

11

As the war continued to crash around us some men in their idle moments took to drinking heavily. Between performing duties in the trenches, picket duties, eating, resting and the odd game of cards there was little else to do. Visits could be made to Balaklava but hot food and other warm pursuits could be very expensive. The day was quite long with an early parade and orders for the day. Breakfast often included a tumbler of rum with more to be had during the afternoon and evening. In some regiments boredom, tinged with cold and fear led to excessive drinking, which in turn might lead to insolent behaviour, insubordination, drunken brawls and to a court martial for the worst offenders, and then to the inevitable floggings or demotions.

In my battalion, perhaps down to the closeness of the Russians there were fewer incidents but all those ills, cholera and other sickness, greatly reduced the effectiveness of our army. On my rounds of the rifle pits I had managed to slap some sense into a few riflemen who had drunk too much and who had let the conditions we all faced get the better of them. There were thankfully no reports of any men deserting from the Brigade. Considering the state of everything over the eight or nine months in the Crimea at that point, it was something of a surprise to me that there wasn't more mayhem across our lines. Maybe there was a good reason for this. Most of our officers in both battalions, though not all, measuring up to the likes of Lieutenant Tryon or Captain Fortune led by example and fought and suffered alongside their men.

They had not wintered at home or in hotels like officers in

some regiments while their men remained in the Crimea. Even Lord Raglan, the commander-in-chief had spent a lot of the winter months on board a ship in Balaklava Harbour, out of danger but more importantly out of sight of the men under his command who were suffering the most.

Slowly, spring was at last on the way. There was a definite change in the Russian weather. The sight of flowers and the sound of birds singing, though some distance away from the sound of rifle or artillery fire was beginning to raise men's spirits. There was even an improvement in our food supply. By the end of March a railway had at long last been completed to bring those goods we needed from our base at Balaklava to the English camps on the Heights. Along with the food came heavy guns and ammunition now being brought by steampower, rather than the sweat of horses and men.

All the movement of artillery was no doubt in preparation for another major bombardment of Sevastopol. The plan, we were informed, was to reduce all of the town's defences with 500 English and French guns. Everything from small 6-pounder field guns to 37 and 68-pounder siege guns.

Obviously all this intense activity could not, and did not, escape the attention of the enemy. We managed to capture a couple of Russians who had either wandered too close in the first day or two of April to our pickets, or had intended deserting anyway. We learned from them that another heavy shelling from our side was expected.

**

This, the Russians believed, would be followed very soon after by another long-anticipated event, the assault by English and French forces on their lines. Our two prisoners then decided that they had had enough already of being on the receiving end of our artillery and definitely deserted.

We could see the enemy below us and they could see us. They were desperately preparing to counter the damage we were about to inflict on them. Additional timber sprouted from their earthworks, extra guns were seen being hauled into position. In their wrecked, roofless churches we could see many candles burning and hear the worshippers as they prayed, no doubt for Divine help. That seemed to come. Their prayers appeared to be answered, albeit temporarily, as very heavy rain began to fall, cloaking the town. Sevastopol looked to vanish as the rain, mixed with black smoke and dense fog, shrouded everything in front of us.

We could hear, in between the crump of falling bombardment shells falling on the town, the despairing screams of people trying to avoid the concentrated fire that because of the rain was just being poured blindly into the town. Artillery fire is neutral about the targets it kills. Fog, wind and smoke may have prevented our gunners from seeing details of the town but it couldn't prevent the damage being done to non-military people.

In their despairing attempts to escape this deadly onslaught, we could hear a mass of people moving away from the southern end of the town. They were heading for the northern part of Sevastopol, to the other side of the harbour at Fort Nicholas.

***

We would discover later that the streets were covered even worse than before with debris, cannon balls and bodies in varying stages of mutilation.

For ten days a constant hail of shells was thrown at the bastions and the buildings, or in some cases heaps of rubble, around the half-circle of defences that protected the town's south side. Over 150,000 shells fell on them, which must have contributed to the killing and injuring of many hundreds.

Not that the Russians just sat back and took the punishment without some retaliation. Our artillery officer, during our recent expedition into Sevastopol had counted over 400 guns and nearly sixty mortars aimed in the allies' direction. Between them they had hurled nearly 90,000 shells and other missiles back at us. Someone obviously had nothing better to do than just count the number of shells arriving and departing.

Our efforts overall though seemed to have made some progress. The fourth bastion looked to be nearly just a heap of rubble and the Mamelon and fifth battery also seemed to have been put out of action. We noticed again that many men were entering the Malakoff, but not coming back out. They must be filling the tunnels and would be likely to reappear just as we attacked, or be called up as reinforcements if our assault waves were able to push the Russians back. Very clever and certainly very deadly!

Furthermore, although we could see obvious damage to the walls of their bastions it seemed a possibility that the tunnels had not really been damaged. An attack on the Redan or Malakoff was not bound to be successful.

As the French had borne the brunt of the fighting so far and were likely to endure heavy losses when they attacked the Malakoff, there was a general feeling filtering down from their camp that their allies should be attempting some really outstanding victory. But if we were to take the Redan we also needed the French to take their main objective, the Malakoff. One couldn't happen without the other.

On the night of the 19th April, we advanced towards the Russian positions just in front of the Quarries. Again I accompanied officers, three of them, Major Rivers, Captain Fortune and Captain Villiers of the Royal Artillery. The RA officer was normally in charge of a forward battery that included 24-pounder howitzers. We also had six riflemen to give covering fire. The Light Division's 77th and 33rd charged their pits and after very heavy hand to hand fighting, captured them. We, in the meantime, in the general melée had managed to move left and forward to get into the town. We all wore the usual array of captured greatcoats over our uniforms. There had been a few changes to our own uniform by this time. The shako had, for practical use, been replaced by a much more comfortable forage cap that at a quick glance could pass for a Russian type. We were also wearing trousers more suited to scrambling over rough ground of which we seemed to be doing quite a lot. They were a dark, sandy-buff in colour of a type of canvas cotton material. It needed to be worn a few times, like boots to be broken in and so made more comfortable. The borrowed greatcoats were long enough to disguise most of these trousers to all but the most intense observer.

***

As retreating Russians began to pass us we joined in the dash for the relative safety of the town's rubble filled streets.

It had seemed to we sergeants, when a few days before we had discussed the situation, that we were not too far away from an all out assault on the Redan. The attack on their positions earlier in the day certainly looked like preparation for this. They were not too far away, and if the Quarry Pits could be taken and held and the French could secure our right flank by their assault and then capture of the Mamelon and the Malakoff, we should then be able to make a big impression on the Great Redan.

As we ran I tried to put these considerations to the back of my mind. We had been joined by an eleventh member of our party. He was a thickset, heavily bearded man. He wore a heavy, black coat that as he ran with us flapped against his calf-length boots. A Russian officer's fur hat was pulled down over his ears. As we reached an abandoned building and took some deep breaths, he was looking us up and down with an expression of disdain in his eyes.

"Russki?" I enquired.

"Da," he replied.

That was all the conversation I would ever have with him as we continued through the town with him leading. As we passed small groups of his rather confused and panic-stricken fellow Russians desperate to return to their billets after being repulsed at the Quarries, he seemed to do little more than grunt at them.

***

These were answered with shrugs and much waving of arms. Was he asking how they had got on in the recent action, or was he preparing a trap for us? I decided that I must try and keep a sharp eye on this particular Johnny Russ.

We moved towards the western edge of what I knew was the Man of War Harbour across a severely damaged quay. By the twisted metal of what could have been a length of railway track we came across what was left of a warehouse. It still had a heavy wooden door. Bits of chain-link were still attached to the hasp. A few feet away lay a large padlock. It looked as though the door had been blown off its hinges. A large pulley wheel, dangling at a perilous angle from a square metal plate that had once held it firmly on the building's second storey, was directly overhead. I very quickly moved out of what would have been its direct route to my head had it chosen that moment to plummet to the ground. I posted sentries after we had hauled the door back into place while adding lengths of timber to the back of it.

The building was large and roofless, with the broken ends of what had been floor supports poking out from the walls just above our heads. Against one wall opposite the door was a ladder. The top of it rested against the sill of a long blasted out window. The walls all around were damaged, but still remained standing high enough to give cover to anyone at the top of the ladder, and looking out from passers-by on the quay below or approaching from the old town. I didn't trust our Russian guide but on the face of it he had chosen our shelter well. I climbed up the ladder to the window ledge and cautiously looked out.

***

I could see lights and the dark shapes of guns in the Russian redoubts up to a thousand paces away. In front of them would be the rising ground from the Quarries towards our camp. Little wonder they could shell us and make life uncomfortable in the rifle pits. A sobering thought swept over me. If where I was standing was such a good vantagepoint, then why weren't their artillery officers here instead of us? Or did they only use it during the hours of daylight?

I descended the ladder and took my thoughts to the three officers.

Major Rivers said, "Yes, curious that but Sergei Ivanovich here," indicating our rather sinister and scowling guide, "assures me that this is now abandoned. It is owned by some prince or other who had the place cleared out and the goods carted away as we moved down from the Alma. Then it was locked and its use forbidden, apparently by orders from the Tsar himself."

After a short pause while he allowed this information to sink in, he continued, "So here we are. I suppose you could say that we are trespassing. In any event we need to be very careful not to draw any attention to this empty property."

He then went on to say, "It would be a good idea, though, when we get back, to make sure it's destroyed in case they change their minds and use it to sight our lines. Captain Villiers can add it to his drawings and notes."

At that Captain Villiers slipped away and began to climb the ladder. Once at the ledge, he withdrew a small notebook and pencil from a linen pouch. After a minute of wriggling to get comfortable he set to work. For about an hour, he remained at the top of the ladder sketching. There was just enough light.

Our side already had detailed drawings of the redoubts from our previous visits to the town. This artillery officer was trying to find out what there was at ground level within their gun pits. That might have been answered by Captain Bantock and his drawings had they, and he, survived.

Those not on sentry duty made themselves as comfortable as possible, at least as much as heaps of broken plaster and bricks would allow. Knapsacks were opened and attention given to breakfast of water, biscuits and dried beef. I took the opportunity to say to Captain Fortune, "Couldn't they just flatten the Redan and Malakoff? Surely we now have enough guns?"

"Yeh, you'd have thought so but they seem to just take it, do a few repairs and be ready again the next day. I think this time we may have to return here, plant a few mines and blow the whole thing up ourselves. That's what poor old Bantock had in mind. I think our artillery man up yonder is of a similar view and just checkin' to see if that's possible. Could be we'll be back here in a week or two."

With that he fell silent. The captain of artillery returned to earth and opened a small pack containing chicken legs and bread.

He then took a long drink from a wine bottle, re-corked it, laid it and the pouch down and sat back, his notebook resting on his chest with his arms folded protectively across it. Then he dropped to sleep. Apart from him, Major Rivers and the Russian, the remaining eight Rifle Brigade took it in turns to mount two-hour guard duties, eat and catch some sleep. One of the riflemen produced a pack of cards so that helped pass the time. Around us came the all too familiar sounds of shells falling, shouts and drum beats as men were summoned to their various tasks. We feared discovery as boots and horses hooves clattered over cobbled streets nearby. It was still difficult to believe that all the activity going on outside was not directed at us. They were though, once more almost certainly preparing for another assault against allied lines.

Captain Fortune, as another salvo passed overhead in the general direction of the movement outside rather than the nearer redoubts, climbed the ladder to check on developments. He dropped down and said,

"Yes, just as we thought. They are gettin' ready to attack. If they are going in daylight in a few more hours' time we should just sit tight. I don't think we could get away with chancin' runnin' with them. We could just as easily be caught in the fire between both sides as we got nearer the Quarries. It's bad enough in the dark, but at least we have a sportin' chance at getting away with it in the confusion, as we've done before. What do you think, sir?" he added, directing his question at Major Rivers.

Captain Villiers and Major Rivers were both awake. The senior officer nodded his head in general agreement but added, "It's vital that we get back as soon as possible. Captain Villiers doesn't think that they have mined the floor of the Redan yet, but they may do so soon. So if our lads can attack before too long that should keep casualties down."

This was good news. It had been feared, especially by those regiments likely to provide men for the first wave of the assault, the forlorn hope, that if they succeeded in capturing this position then the retreating Russians would be likely to detonate pre-laid explosive mines. These were detested by all assault waves. Artillery shells they could usually hear coming and might be able to take action to avoid them. They could almost accept them as a normal part of war. Facing a man with rifle and bayonet was also expected and gave an opponent an even chance, but being thrown in the air by an unseen exploding mine was something quite different.

Captain Villiers explained how such weapons could be very easily made and used.

"All you do," he said, "is find a hole in rocky ground. Easy hereabouts. Fill it with gunpowder. Do the same with a keg or a mortar shell, add the powder and throw in as many musket balls or nails, and add scraps of metal. You then cover it with soil and set it off through a length of tin tube hidden in the ground or covered in grass, or even connect them to a fuse in your mine and set it off by 'electricity' through cable some distance away. Then you have your big bang."

Just as he finished his bomb making lesson, the door of the warehouse began to shake. We had added extra wood to barricade it. Had we been discovered? No, surely they would have just fired a field gun into the warehouse or just rushed up with infantry.

The door was being pushed violently. Fortunately, our efforts had concentrated on protecting this door, the only way in. So far it was withstanding the attack on it.

The riflemen, without being told to had formed a semicircle some ten paces from the door. Their left hands cupping the barrels of their rifles while the right moved the hammer to the half-cock position. If the door did suddenly give way then whoever was on the outside was in for a really nasty surprise. A few pieces of timber and several bricks clattered to the floor and the door moved a few inches. The tension lifted as a voice called out, softly in Russian.

Captain Fortune motioned most of the riflemen to the other side of the door while he and rifleman Bains stepped forward a few paces.

Two figures, one breathless after his exertions against the door, entered. One was a soldier, the other a woman. Fortune threw him to the floor and plunged a rifle-sword into his throat. Bains threw his rifle across to another man and seized the frightened woman.

He thrust an arm round her neck and a hand over her mouth.

Captain Fortune whispered in French to our Russian to tell her to be quiet and stop struggling. Our guide looked even more disagreeable than usual. Rifleman Metcalfe produced a length of rope. She was tied securely and placed in a far corner of the room. While this had been going on I had placed myself at the door. Another of our men had climbed the ladder. As far as he could tell there had been no response to our actions.

The body of the dead soldier was thrown in another corner, while we waited for the comparative safety that night would bring. The large space we were in with no windows only had the light from the roofless void above our heads, but it seemed to be taking an age for night to fall.

Then we heard the scrunch of approaching boots. Another visitor! We had replaced the door and set rifleman Andrews on alert for any suspicious movement or sound. He had thrown a small piece of brick into our group as we waited anxiously for the comfort that the night would bring. We had though, heard the boots at about the same time as Andrews had and were preparing to act. It was a little surprising then, when a rather polite knocking began on the door. Then a voice calling softly, possibly a name that sounded like, Katya, followed by a stream of Russian in a rather more vexed tone.

"He's here to see the woman," announced Major Rivers.

I had rather thought that might be the reason.

"Sergei Ivanovich here confirms it," continued Rivers.

"My Russian's good but not when they go on a bit. Open the door very carefully, Andrews. Let's see who our guest is," as he eased his revolver from its holster.

Andrews and Bains carefully moved the door ajar and a man burst in. He appeared to be alone. He rushed excitedly forward not appearing to notice our two guardians at the entrance, and ran straight on to the sword fixed to rifleman Metcalfe's Enfield. There was a gasp, much of surprise as of the noise of him expiring. His body was placed beside that of the other Russian soldier.

Rivers stepped towards the woman. "I'd better ask her a few questions to see what's going on."

At that our living Russian stepped forward and quickly moved in front of him and whispered to Major Rivers.

"He's going to question her. His Russian's better than mine and she is more likely, he thinks, to speak to him, a fellow Russian, than us, the enemy."

Captain Fortune, with that strain of amusement in his voice, added what I and probably the rest of us had been thinking, anyway.

"I've a good idea what's been goin' on here, or would have, had we not spoiled their plans."

Muffled conversation from the corner of the room where the woman lay, followed. The Russian returned and spoke quietly to both officers, in French.

"It seems that our two dead beauties decided to have a fling with the woman there before the main attack that begins at nine this evening. Just in case it proved to be their last! There wasn't time to go to her usual place before they were likely to be ordered forward, so they arranged to meet her here. The first about 5:00 p.m. and the second one, half-hour or so later," Major Rivers said. "He is," indicating our guide, "very uneasy. He believes that if we release her she'll give us away. He is not looking forward to being taken by his own people."

"Well," said Captain Fortune resolutely, "we'll leave her tied-up here. Give her some coins and then tell her to forget that she has seen us. She can explain away the ropes however she likes. Assumin'," he added, "she's ever found!"

The Russian moved back to the corner and knelt down beside her. The considerable bulk of his body and his coat completely shielding her from our view in the evening's gloom. It was also soon time for us to go and we collected our equipment, looked carefully around to make sure we had left nothing to give away the fact that English soldiers had even been there, and made ready to leave.

Our guide had moved away from the woman by the time the rest of our party had collected by the door waiting for the order to move off. As far as I could see in the gloomy atmosphere now coating the room, the woman was very still, probably still frightened for her life. I thought little more of her condition; there were more immediate matters to deal with.

Outside, the wet, smoke-laden evening air began to fill with the sound of artillery shells, the beat of drums, bugle calls and hoarse voices shouting orders. The evening dullness lit once more by bursts of flame from cannon fire and rifles, as they spat out death.

Captain Fortune and the Russian led the way, then three riflemen abreast, followed by the two other officers. Captain Villiers followed, with his hand across his chest where his pouch with the maps and drawings was hidden, the other hand clutching his revolver under this greatcoat and the three other riflemen and me in a staggered line brought up the rear. We tried desperately not to look like a skirmish line of English light infantry on patrol. Did we look more Russian being part of a rag-bag of eleven, or more conspicuous the last time when there had been just the three of us? Perhaps we did look a queer sight trying to look like Russian soldiers on their way to attack English positions.

We followed other men moving down, and crossed the southern end of the harbour towards a gap in the semi-circle of defences between the Garden and Barrack Batteries. Ahead of us some five hundred yards away we could just make out ghost-like figures, as light from shellfire reflected off the bayonets of the first wave of the Russians heading towards the Quarries. To our left shells from the Great Redan were hurtling towards our lines to keep English heads down as their infantry advanced.

The enemy we had joined was part of the second wave.

**

It was doubtful that we would just be able to pass through this line without being shot at by our own side. We might just be able to merge in with the first wave if they were pushed back. There was always chaos and confusion at such a time. This had served us very well before. Around sixty Russians from the first wave had started to retreat. A hand signal from one of our officers urged us to go right. At this, our guide moved towards some rocks and then vanished into the night. We followed, yet just as we reached the eastern end of a ridge a voice challenged us, but as Captain Fortune prepared to answer, shots followed.

"Run for your lives," he yelled, as about thirty Russians charged us with their bayonets levelled menacingly. We riflemen fired at them. Four or five enemy men fell at once, but the rest carried on towards us. Without bothering to re-load, there would not have been time anyway, even for us, we turned and ran, following Captain Villiers and Major Rivers who were already showing much speed. The surviving Russians continued their pursuit.

I then noticed a very heavy breathing Captain Fortune trying to keep up. After a few more unsteady and laboured steps he fell against a rock. I turned towards him and pulled him around the other side of it, away from the charging Russians who continued after the others.

My company commander had been hit at least twice. Once, just above the ankle and a second ball had hit his left arm just on the point of his elbow. His face was wracked with pain. I removed my belt with some difficulty and wrapped it as quickly as I could around his arm just below his armpit.

***

Somehow he managed to push himself round to face me and then he spoke haltingly.

"Leave me, Jack. Save yourself," he managed to say through clenched teeth.

I reached forward and rested my rifle on a rock and looked at his arm. I had managed to stem the flow of blood from that wound. All that remained of his arm just below my makeshift tourniquet were bits of shattered bone and sinew, with strips of coat. The mess that a few minutes before had been his elbow, was only really held together by the stickiness of his blood, acting like glue on the shattered remains. I ripped off my sergeant's sash from under my Russian infantryman's coat and tied it around the remains of his arm.

"Can you move?" I asked.

"No, I'm done for. Go! I'm orderin' you to leave me. Give me my revolver, then go."

I looked around, scrabbled on the ground and found it. I poked my little finger in the muzzle to make sure it hadn't been stopped up with mud then tucked the Colt into my shirt. If I had to use the revolver on the way back I didn't want it blowing up in my face.

"Go!" he repeated.

I looked at him. By now he had slumped to the ground and looked at me pleadingly as I bent down beside him.

"Leave me, Jack. You can do nothing."

"No, Captain James. I'll carry you. You once did me a kindness. I've not forgotten. Do you remember the river and that day in the library? You could have reported me to your father or given me a thrashing yourself, but you didn't. You have always treated me well, even gave me books. Then there was South Africa and now here, in the Crimea. Now it's my chance to help you."

Then he spoke again, his face trying to smile but showing much strain as waves of delirium appeared to be taking over, or so I thought.

"She saw you!"

"She saw me?" I repeated. "What do you mean, sir? Who saw what, when?" But he was unconscious.

Then concentrating on the task to come, I grabbed my rifle, took off the sword, replaced it in its scabbard and then smashed the butt of the Enfield and the hammer against a rock. Hammer and sights went flying, and splintered wood was sent in various directions. I would have done the same to Captain Fortune's rifle had I been able to find it, but dare not risk the time that might take. I threw away the rest of my weapon, comforting myself with the thought that no Russian would be able to use it against allied soldiers. In all, this had probably taken a minute or so, but to my relief the Russians who had first confronted us seemed to have remained in hot pursuit of the rest of the party. Musket, and rifle fire exchanges were going on all around so I could not tell if this involved them or not.

I turned my attention to the badly injured man lying with his head slumped at my feet. It was good that some of an officer's usual equipment had been left behind at camp. I cut off his sword-bayonet with my own sword and removed all the other items of uniform that might chafe or make unnecessary noise. Then, with a great heave, I lifted him upright and then managed to get his chest resting across my shoulders. He made very little sound, other than a kind of whimpering, but at least he was still breathing. I could also feel a very faint breath on the back of my neck as I half carried and dragged him towards our lines.

I decided that I should veer slightly right towards the French left and avoid if possible, any Russians still retreating from the Quarries. I was beginning to lose all track of time and feared I might be losing all sense of direction too, as a feeling of wooziness was coming and going. I had been staggering forward for a few minutes when I crashed over the body of Captain Villiers. I sat up, Captain Fortune had fallen off my back and to the right as I had blundered into the prone Artillery officer. I reached forward and felt inside the dead man's tunic, grabbed the notebook and maps and tucked the pouch containing them inside my shirt next to the revolver. A few paces to the left and right of the dead man lay the bodies of four riflemen. Each had numerous wounds all over them. Their swords showed bloody evidence, as did the corpses of a similar number of Russians nearby, of their attempts at defending Captain Villiers to the bitter end. Taking a deep breath I again managed to hoist the wounded officer onto my back.

**

Ten more tortured paces forward and I passed the body of Major Rivers but I decided, reluctantly, that I had better not stop again for fear of collapsing myself, as waves of light-headedness were sweeping over me. I moved as quickly as I could at the risk of running into Russians retreating from their clashing with our pickets. I scrambled over rocky terrain, lungs heaving at the strain of it all. Captain Fortune was still breathing but still unconscious; at least he was spared the pain my involuntary dropping him must have caused, and the jolting he must be getting as I hauled us both forward across stones and boulders. I heard the sound of voices, English, sweet English ones!

I had reached the edge of our lines and could hear our advanced pickets. I yelled out hoarse with fatigue, "Rifles returning. Hold your fire."

Soldiers of the 23rd Fusiliers seized my passive casualty. Then rough hands grabbed at me. I was exhausted and had fallen forward into a shallow trench. I was pulled on to a stretcher.

"See to him first. He's badly shot up. Take him to the surgeon," I managed to gasp out before unconsciousness swept over me, as well as my company commander.

When I regained my senses, I found myself in my quarters among the all too familiar sounds and smells of camp life.

Lieutenant Axelby stood before me.

"Bit of a rough do then, Finch," he said, "rifleman Metcalfe told us what happened and your part in it. Jolly good show and well done to you."

"Any news of Captain Fortune?" I said, my voice croaking with concern and thirst.

"Didn't make it I'm afraid. Got to the surgeon's but was too badly hurt. Sorry! Damned fine officer. And I know he had a very high opinion of you. The colonel's very pleased with your efforts. He's putting you up for a medal and there'll probably be promotion too I shouldn't wonder."

The lieutenant meant well but I was feeling very bruised and low and certainly ached all over. A medal wouldn't replace a man I felt respect for, liked, although we had very little in common, and certainly admired. The lieutenant, though, in trying to raise my spirits was certainly right in one respect in that the captain had certainly been a fine officer. He would be much missed by all the men in his company.

Just as I sank back on my cot, I reached inside my tunic, but the sketchpad and maps had gone.

"Don't worry," added Mr. Axelby, "it's already been taken to the commander-in-chief's headquarters. Should be jolly useful." With that he left.

The next day, still rather dazed and certainly still aching, I was ordered to the battalion commander's quarters. I was tired, but thought I should try and make some effort to present myself as smartly as I could muster. I rummaged around in my meagre clothes store and found a presentable shirt, tunic, and borrowed a sergeant's sash and belt.

"You and the men did very well, Finch. I believe you've already been told that I'm putting you up for a medal and there'll be promotion as well."

I thanked him, saluted and left, if a little unsteadily. I was still not convinced that our recent journey into enemy territory had been much of a success. Three officers killed as well as four good riflemen.

12

We were eventually told that an artillery bombardment would begin on the 6th June. We hoped that the plans would include a successful attack from the eastern end of the pits held by us to take the Quarries. This would have the effect of reducing the distance between us and the Redan. That, after the French success we all assumed would take place at the Mamelon and then the Malakoff. Damage was continually being inflicted on the redoubts but, as I had observed from the warehouse in Sevastopol, they were still more than capable of disrupting an allied assault.

The latest deafening bombardment did begin on the 6th June, as promised and lasted until six that same evening. As we waited for the order to attack we saw Lord Raglan sat astride his horse not too far away.

"Waiting for General Pelissier to join him so they can give the order to advance," said Major Deed-Valentine.

An order was issued for the French to go, but this seemed odd as the French general had not been seen.

But off they went, cheering and shouting as they moved along the ravines. Once more the Zouaves were leading the assault heading first for the ditch, then up to the imposing walls of the Mamelon rising so formidably above their heads. Again, heavy musket and artillery fire greeted the French who really had no other option but to fall back. Their officers had to rush at them in a bid to encourage them to renew their attack.

***

The Zouaves, to their very great credit, managed to cross the ditch again and were soon forcing their way up the walls. Somehow, even without ladders and under constant, heavy fire they still managed to reach the parapet. We watched amazed and impressed as they dropped from the top of the wall on to the floor of the Mamelon below. After a very short delay, during which time I supposed them to be spiking every gun they could lay their hands on, they suddenly reappeared on the other side of the bastion. Then off they went again screaming at the enemy. The Russians had been slow to respond to being thrown out of the position and seeing Frenchmen taking over the floor of the work. Now the Zouaves were advancing into the space between that position and the Malakoff. Shells and musket fire began to pour into them. Sheets of flame and smoke temporarily swept across this ground and shrouded the attackers. Then they faced lines of Russian bayonets charging at them from the Malakoff. For a second or two the French just stood there as if uncertain whether to go forward and rush into a superior force of Russians now nearly upon them. Then they turned and ran back to the Mamelon. The ones nearest the enemy being the first to have Russian cold steel plunged into their backs. The Zouaves weren't given any time to recover and re-form. Successive waves of the enemy drove home their advantage. The French were now in some disarray and were scrambling into the Mamelon then running desperately across its floor and up and over the opposite parapet they had so recently and bravely attacked and captured.

***

In total disorder, aided by Russian gunfire they dropped back down the walls, across the ditch and back towards their own lines. They had failed, a glorious failure but a brave attempt, and we cheered their efforts with much enthusiasm.

We rushed the Quarries recently retaken by them, perhaps inspired by what we had seen. A small enemy force was easily pushed out. Then things began to change. Reinforcements from their tunnels under the Great Redan, no doubt also encouraged by the way they had seen their own side defeat the Zouave attack on the Mamelon, fell on us. For two hours we pushed each other in and out of these pits. Both sides sending in reinforcements. The fighting soon descended into hand to hand encounters. It was only in the morning, around 5 a.m., that yet another Russian attack was repulsed. All around us lay dead and wounded in heaps.

While we were bitterly disputing ownership of the Quarry Pits, the French had launched another attack on the Mamelon and another enemy defensive position nearer to the main harbour.

We attempted to snatch a quick breakfast during the lull when both sides seemed to be reorganising. Then one of our lookouts shouted that the Russians had hauled up a white flag in their lines, which by now were only some 250 paces from us.

By the time the truce came into effect, at midday we noticed a white flag also flying over the Mamelon. Sadly, not their surrender! We could see French casualties lying around in great numbers. Little surprise really when it was later confirmed that they had suffered over 7,000 killed and wounded.

As stretcher-bearers from both sides scurried among the fallen in an all too familiar repeat of their work we saw officers once again, from both sides, offering each other flasks of brandy and cigars. Instead of yet another chapter in this series of bloody battlefields it could have been the scene of officers preparing to ride off to the local hunt. I supposed that brave deeds are admired and respected by all soldiers, no matter which side performs them. Regardless of the grim sight of the casualties strewn all about us, men's spirits seem to have lifted. So too, had thoughts that what we had achieved by retaking and holding the Quarry Pits would only serve to hasten the day when a full assault would be needed against the Great Redan, Malakoff and Mamelon if the town was to be taken and the war ended. Attacks meant casualties and many of them. The Russians surely would now be even more aware of our intentions after this day's work. They were now more likely to be very determined to keep us out.

"Are we gaining anything, sergeant?" asked rifleman Wightman. "All the Froggies and us seem to be doing is giving the Russkis target practice. We get so far then they push us back. The next day we do the same again. When's it going to finish?"

"We will get there," I said, pointing into the town. "They have good positions but they can't hold out forever."

I couldn't really tell him what I thought about our situation. The delays, the mistakes, the casualties had already made morale drop like a stone.

Telling a man he faced almost certain death having to climb the sheer walls of the Redan could not help matters.

"Let's hope we're all still alive to see us take the town, then," said a familiar and very gloomy voice behind me.

After morning parade on the 11th June and dismissal, I returned to my shared bivouac. Several minutes later, rifleman Towers appeared at the tent flap. To call my dwelling a tent was not strictly accurate. After most of our tents had been destroyed in the November hurricane we had set to, in an effort to prevent future attacks by nature. We had eventually dug or scraped a trench about a foot across and to about the same depth in the iron-hard ground. We then placed some salvaged tent poles in each of the four corners of our roughly square-shaped enclosure and then mounted a larger pole in the centre. Lengths of scrap canvas were then tied from this pole to the sides. A variety of animal skins collected from the French slaughterhouses in Kamiesh were then thrown over the canvas. We had to discard most of them though with the arrival of spring. Along with the rise in temperature had come a rise in the smell.

When a supply of wood did eventually come up from Balaklava for building huts we used it to make walls and a door. Sometimes it did get a bit too cosy in there with four of us sharing so we added a canvas flap to the door, which allowed it to be kept aired and less stuffy on sunny, friendlier days. Our intention had been to try and copy our battalion commander's hut. We may have not quite achieved that but it sufficed. We had quarried some large stones and built a low wall all around, apart from the door opening.

These held the walls in place at the bottom and we were able to nail the tops of the walls to the poles. It was a strange thing about nails that rather summed up what life was like in the Crimea. For a long time the Commissariat would not release a supply of nails unless the order was for a tonne of them. All most of us needed for building huts were a few handfuls. Several of our officers had managed to get around this odd, rather stupid rule. Too often the Commissariat had dithered, not unlike the way the high command had dithered on military matters, not merely in the way they had issued nails but in the way they had distributed other supplies including food. A situation that had not escaped the pen of Mr. Russell of *The Times*.

We had also attempted to dig smaller channels running out from our main hut trench system to drain rainwater and melting snow. Our lodging may not have always been warm, but did at the very least keep out the worst of the winter's weather. Fortunately none of us who shared these quarters had fallen victim to frostbite, but nights during December, January and February had been cold with only thin, summer issue blankets and a greatcoat to keep the cold at bay.

Towers had pulled back the tent flap, knocked on our wooden door and sauntered in to the billet.

"Sergeant Finch, you're wanted at battalion headquarters."

I buttoned my tunic, put my sash over my shoulder, making sure the tassels were hanging correctly. Then eased the crimson girdle into position and buckled my belt across it.

***

I reached for my remaining pair of gloves, which I decided were too worn to be worth wearing. Then I took my Kilmarnock bonnet with its tuft showing signs of wear. I usually only wore it at morning parade and generally kept it on the butt of my upturned rifle with its fixed sword that I had driven about 15 of its 17 inch blade into about the only soft piece of soil I had managed to find in the Heights. This was a simple form of hat stand but more usefully, kept rifle and sword in easy reach in case of a surprise attack. For day-to-day wear I favoured a forage cap, not unlike my Kilmarnock, but which, at a quick glance, was so much like the Russian one, especially in the fading light we had used to creep into the town. A brief look in a piece of mirror we had found in one of the shattered farmhouses at the foot of the Sapoune Hills and I was ready to report to the Colonel.

I strode purposefully into the crisp and clear morning air. A change from the smoky or foggy atmosphere nearer the town. I reached the senior officer's hut and knocked.

"Enter," said the voice of my commanding officer, who sat at his table, a sketch map of the town's defences in front of him.

"Finch, you know as much as any man that we have to move on the Redan soon from our position in the Quarries. You'll also be very well aware that if the French don't capture the Mamelon and then the Malakoff then that puts us really up against it. The Russians can throw everything at us."

It was heading for me. I knew it. I had that tightening of the chest. Something was going to be thrown at me.

I had that same sort of feeling that I got just before an attack.

I had been very lucky, but how long could that last? I stood and waited and was then waved to a chair.

"What we are planning to do is to send a party in and disable their guns and cause as much mischief as possible. Captain Villier's drawings, and thanks for bringing them back, confirm the strength of their defences. We've had limited success in blasting holes in parts of it but they recover very well. They're able to bring up reinforcements from thin air. His notes give us detailed information about the tunnels, but we don't seem able to exactly pin-point and destroy their maze of workings even with our largest 68-pounders. We also know from one of our spies that they've had one of their top engineers, a chap called Todleben, sortin' out their positions. Our French allies had hoped to undermine the Russian trenches, but had to give up digging their own tunnels before they could cause any real damage to the enemy. If we are to stand any chance of success not only must as many of their guns as possible be put out of action, but the tunnels where their reinforcements will be hiding before they can help their men in the Redan, need to be sealed. If we can only delay them long enough while they dig themselves out, it should give just enough time to take and hold it while the French seize their two objectives."

This was a wide-ranging and fact-filled speech building up to what I strongly suspected was my being asked to go into Sevastopol again. He had given many reasons, which would make my refusing the task very difficult. Always supposing I was going to be offered the choice.

***

All I could think about though was how increasingly difficult and costly these missions were becoming. I studied the map. Could we risk it again? Going into town once more was bad enough but this time carrying enough powder to blow enemy guns, embrasures, tunnel entrances and possibly us, sky high! All this without being challenged, captured or killed. The Russians had made similar attempts against some of our artillery batteries but had failed with great losses. Would our party fare better? Were our pickets more alert or were the Russians just unlucky? Could we really get into town again, create enough of a diversion or enough damage to give our soldiers less chance of being slaughtered in large numbers when the main attacks began?

Again and again these same questions were repeated over and over in my mind while I looked at the sketch map. Why hadn't navy and artillery guns managed more of a destructive result? Were our gunners or munitions not good enough? We had all felt the draught as our shells had whined and whistled above our heads on their way towards Russian lines. It was just very difficult to understand why our heavy bombardments hadn't completely flattened the town and its defences, or at the very least landed a few shells on the tunnels to keep their hidden forces corked up like wine in a bottle.

I found myself scratching my chin as I stood there weighing up the odds.

Then a Royal Navy lieutenant, an officer of the Royal Artillery and a French officer, Captain Didierjean, who had been a friend of Captain Fortune, entered the quarters.

Bringing up the rear was that same Russian who had been our guide on my earlier expedition.

"This is Sergeant Finch. He's been into town a few times. Knows his way around," said the Colonel.

At this, each of the other officers nodded a greeting while Sergei Ivanovich merely grunted what I took to be his acknowledgement. I moved a little from the table to give them a better sight of the map.

"We need to time this perfectly. Go too early and they may have time to repair any damage we do. Ideally, it would be more productive if we could arrange a big bang just before our men attack," offered the Artillery officer.

I had been thinking the same thing. Do the job and get out before the customary bombardment begins before the assault. I then wondered why a naval officer was present although they had supplied, and were manning, some navy guns on the Heights and did occasionally bring ships' guns to bear on the town from their anchorage. We only needed Royal Marines and Cavalry officers to make the suit complete.

The Russian in the meantime, had moved closer to the table and, speaking in French, seemed to be drawing lines across the map with his right index finger. It looked to be indicating a point a little above where the enemy had sunk four or five ships to block off the western entrance to Sevastopol Harbour. This had effectively prevented any seaborne attack against the forts that lined the harbour.

The finger then moved across the map to a spot on the northern side of the harbour just below Star Fort and to the west of Fort Catherine. From there it crossed the bay and stopped between the two forts that guard either side of the entrance to the Man of War Harbour. Just south of where he had stopped was roughly where the warehouse, which we had used as a base was situated. Then the finger continued towards the south-western end of this harbour near that very spot.

"If you go on the evening of the 13th June, tomorrow night, and can have your equipment in place by 2:00 a.m. the next day, that is a few hours before the bombardment and then frontal assault begins, then this should add to the destruction. It will also keep reinforcements occupied when our men overrun their objectives."

It sounded easy as the Colonel outlined what I had more or less already been told.

"Well, Finch, you've been our man on the ground. What do you think?"

I thought that it was nothing short of madness but decided that wasn't what anyone else in the room wanted to hear. Before I could answer, he added, "You'll have probably realised, Sergeant," nodding at the naval officer, "that we have a different route planned for getting the party into town. Instead of you all going through the usual gap between the Garden and Barrack batteries, the idea is to come in from the direction of the main harbour."

"Is there a chance, sir, of a bombardment on those two batteries to create a diversion about the time we'll be crossing the harbour?" I asked, a little surprised at myself in asking such a question.

"We'll have a word with the Navy and the Artillery and send in a few men as a feint against one of those positions," replied the colonel. He continued, "A launch will take the party from Balaklava Harbour and drop it just to the north of Fort Constantine, opposite the enemy blockade ships. Then a short walk across the peninsula to a point to the south and west of Star Fort. We anticipate they won't be expecting any allied activity from that side of the town. All their guns and the infantry in the barracks, halfway down, face towards the north and east where an attack against the Star Fort would be most likely to come from. Sergei Ivanovich has assured me that there is very little activity around the strip of beach from Constantine to just below the barracks."

He looked at me and the others, confident that the plan was well thought out. It certainly sounded likely to succeed.

"From there small boats provided by Sergei's tame Tatars will take you across the bay and down to the warehouse quay. Once all equipment has been removed, the boats will be holed and sunk. The Tatars will also provide wagons to take you all and your supplies to within a very short distance of the Redan and the Malakoff. The force will be split between the two redoubts. There is, according to our Russian friend here a lot of coming and going of men, wagons and horses. So a few more are unlikely to be challenged. If you time your arrival correctly, you catch them at guard change. Not at their best so early in the morning. Set the charges as near the magazines as possible spike a few guns and go. Sergei Ivanovich will lead you through the old town and out by number six bastion and then down towards the lines of the French left. The artillery barrage put up as a diversion will help you get clear.

"Then the main bombardment will begin and most Russians will have more pressing things to do than pursue you through the French pickets. Then the French right will begin their assault on the Mamelon and the Malakoff. This will be followed by our attack on the Redan.

"As before, you should be well clear but the French will be alerted of your approach."

The meeting continued, with the action expected by each man in more detail being discussed. The naval lieutenant with eight blue jackets will be supervising the boats across the bay and on into the Man of War Harbour. Then they help with the equipment. The Artillery was providing an officer, four gunners, the powder, and be in charge also of five sappers from the Royal Sappers and Miners. This party would lay mines, spike guns and carry out whatever other damage they could manage. The Rifle Brigade's contribution was to be Lieutenant Anderson, who the Colonel had briefed earlier, six riflemen and me. Our job was to provide covering fire as and when needed. We would also be probing ahead to see if the coast was clear. This suited me as I still did not trust our Russian guide.

In overall, command was the French officer, Capitain Didierjean. Twenty-eight men in all, with Tatars assisting with the boats and wagons. Our Russian spy would go on ahead and check any changes in the enemy guard duties.

What seemed only a few hours later, but was 3:00 p.m. the following day, the 13th June, we eight of the Brigade began the walk down to Balaklava. Lieutenant Anderson, me and riflemen Williams, Metcalfe, Sellers, Knowles, Downing and Forman. Much to my surprise, Williams and Metcalf had volunteered. When I asked them why, they had told me they had a few scores to settle for the loss of some of their comrades. We raised a few eyebrows and a few cheers as we passed various regiments dressed as we were in Russian infantrymen's tunics. It was still light, but by the time we landed above Sevastopol Harbour it would not be too far off night. Dark enough, we hoped, to pass muster as any other Russians.

We boarded a steam launch along with the rest of the similarly dressed members of our party. The boat chugged at a little over normal walking pace speed from the harbour, past Cape Chersonese and duly we were put ashore on the northern side of Sevastopol Harbour. This was as planned but the three hours it had taken meant that we could not afford to waste any time. We now had a very different view of the town from the one that we usually saw. There were still the occasional shell bursts that lit up the sky and provided a little light for us to move off and head past Fort Constantine and towards Fort Michael quite quickly, or as fast as the terrain allowed. We moved down towards the beach where we were due to meet Ivanovich and his Tatars.

As the rest of the party dropped down towards the shoreline, Lieutenant Anderson pulled us back to form a covering line on the shingle further up the beach. Just in case there was the odd Russian patrol wandering around from Star Fort or the barracks, as the boats were being loaded. A few minutes later Capitain Didierjean joined us and said that so far there were no boats. He suggested he and I go and scour left and right along the beach to see if we were in the wrong place to meet the Tatars and their boats. I went right, picking my way carefully over a beach that shelved away gently towards the shoreline. I had fixed my sword and advanced with rifle at the half-cock, in case the sound of my boots on the shingle made such a noise that could be heard way off. I strained to hear, but there was nothing nearby just the sound of stones crunching under my feet and the all too familiar companion of Sevastopol under siege and the faint lapping of the waves a few paces away. I walked to just short of Fort Michael and could see lanterns flashing in the distance. I found nothing but decided not to try my luck by continuing. So, I returned to where I had left Lieutenant Anderson and his men. Perhaps the Frenchman had fared better. But no, as he approached I sensed he had found nothing also. He whispered there was nothing, no boats, Tatars or guide.

At that moment, we heard the unmistakable sound of approaching shells. Some were certainly falling among the group at the water's edge. A large explosion then occurred close to us and the draught from it blew the nine of us off our feet. Fortunately for us, the layer of sand beneath the shingle had taken most of the force of the blast, though we were showered in pebbles.

***

My ears were ringing, my head was banging and for a few moments I felt quite dazed. As my head began to clear, I got up grabbed my rifle and went off staggering down towards the water's edge where we had left the others. Where most of them had been standing was just a smouldering depression. Bits of body, uniform, shreds of equipment lay scattered in and around the shell hole. The explosion made worse by detonating some of the powder they had been carrying. Other kegs had been thrown some distance away. Had they all gone up we would also have been caught in the blast and killed in one massive bang. Most of them were dead. A few, sheltered by the men blown apart in the explosion, lay burnt black with horrible scorch marks across their bodies. Uniforms had been ripped off and pieces lay smouldering all around. I could do nothing for any of them so I made to return to the rifle party further up the beach. Further shells came in, whining mercilessly over my head as I threw myself down on the stones hoping to avoid hot splinters of metal flying all too close. Desperately, I begun to crawl away to where they were waiting anxiously.

"All dead or soon will be. Didn't stand a chance," I reported.

"We need to go," said the French officer. "Let's go up towards the fort and bear left at the barracks. They may at any moment be sending men down to see if anyone has survived."

Off we went, keeping as low as possible. Beach gave way to scrub-covered rough, rocky ground. Didierjean was right. A force of infantrymen was moving down to our right, towards the beach.

Then I caught sight of a familiar figure standing at the open door of a barrack block. He was a perfect target.

"Reckon you could get him, sergeant?" asked Lieutenant Anderson, "I wondered where he'd gone. The swine's betrayed us."

Captain Didierjean did look a little doubtful. He realised that if I fired, it might be enough to bring them all down on our heads. On the other hand, he had caused our mission to fail and was responsible for the deaths of good men. As for the reason why he had done this, well, he was a Russian, but he'd been paid and this was not the place for reasons or excuses.

"Go ahead, Sergeant," said the Frenchman, "*bonne chance.*"

The Russian still stood in the doorway as though he was waiting for the men now moving on to the beach for survivors to return and report the success of his betrayal to him.

I removed the sword from my Enfield rifle, checked that all was well with it, adjusted the rear sight, pulled the hammer back to full cock, raised it to my shoulder, took aim and fired. Sergei Ivanovich fell dead.

We moved quickly on, heading east once we were clear and

out of range of the Star Fort's artillery. We needed to cross the Mckenzie Heights, avoiding their lines, cross the River Charnaya and then swing right and head back to the Heights overlooking Sevastopol.

On our return, Lieutenant Anderson went off to report to our battalion commander that the mission was a failure.

Before returning to his own camp, Capitain Didierjean thanked us for our efforts, gravely saluted and left. The rest of us returned to the sanctuary of our billets.

13

Whether it was our failure, or Ivanovich's treachery that brought about a postponement of the attack on the Redan to the 18th June, really made very little difference. The Russians must have known that an attack was only a matter of time following our massive bombardments. And what they did not know had now probably been supplied by intelligence from Sergei Ivanovich. It was also very difficult to hide the level of noise and excitement from men as they prepared for an attack. Apart from the cleaning and general care of weapons, which in truth were fairly quiet tasks, nothing could disguise the creaking of gun carriage wheels, or the labouring of horses as guns were pulled into position.

The Russians too, were not exactly quiet as they took up their positions in the gun pits. We also knew that there had been desertions from the French camp. After previous failures they certainly were not looking forward to rushing the Mamelon or Malakoff. They may have shared information with the Russians in exchange for safe passage out of Sevastopol. In some ways I could hardly blame them for trying to avoid the coming battle and its inevitable slaughter. French casualties, almost everyone seemed to agree were bound to be very high. Even bribes of extra money and the promise of quick promotion did not provide them with enough incentive to once again risk life and limb in what numbers of the besieging force were thinking, was not going to succeed. Why should it? It hadn't up to now!

A promoted man with money in his pocket is not really

much help if he is dead. As we looked across to the French camp there was again that expectant feeling of doom in the air. It was not unknown for men of the first wave, not generally expected to survive in any great numbers, to tie labels around their necks with names and addresses giving details of wives or mothers in case the worst happened. I had been over in their camp once before when I had seen this being done. Now I sat in my own billet imagining this happening. Men scribbling away on little pieces of card. Not really very good for morale!

Our orders informed us that the French would begin the attack first, at 6:00 a.m. on Monday, the 18th June. Not the date that I would have chosen had I been born in France, as it marked the fortieth anniversary of their defeat at Waterloo. Their assault would begin after a three-hour bombardment.

Then the French were told to stand down and we were told to do the same. For some reason, unexplained, there was a delay.

More confused orders reached us. Our allies would begin their move forward at 3.00 a.m. just before sunrise. This would give them some protection against starting in daylight. They had been ready to go earlier, or as ready as any men could be facing shell and shot and the delay must be adding to already frayed nerves. It also gave our own prophets of doom more ammunition.

"Whose side is the French commander on?" asked Williams, only for Lieutenant Anderson to advise him to keep such views to himself.

Then, suddenly, a rocket was fired and the French surged forward. But apparently this was too soon as a second one soon followed. This was the correct signal for the attack to begin. The sky lit up, flooding all around in an orangey light. It also marked out rather too clearly the blue uniforms of the 97th who were leading the charge. Concentrated fire from the Russians tore into them, ripping ladders, ropes, planks and other assault equipment from their grasp. A few of the French infantry were able to break through but were soon cut to pieces in the crossfire between the Redan and Malakoff redoubts.

We had also begun to move forward and were trying to see what we could do with our rifles to support the French.

At 5.30 a.m. the rest of our assault troops, the 33rd Foot, the 57th and Captain Stuart's company, including that Norfolk sergeant of the Rifle Brigade, began to move out from the safety of the Quarries. Many of them carried ladders for the climbing of those steep Redan Walls. My fellow sergeant passed within a few feet of where I was standing, firing into the Malakoff. I raised one arm in salute and shouted good luck as he charged past me yelling encouragement and urging the company forward. As Captain Stuart and the others moved on, they too, were met with withering fire. Many of our first wave were hit and even the musket balls that missed, smashed into hard ground sending up sparks, earth and splinters of rock. Men were desperately trying to wipe their faces free of these tiny, but deadly scraps. Some tumbled forward, others tried to run to their left or right in blind panic.

All I knew for sure was another company of riflemen including me were trying to keep the heads of Russian gunners down while the attack continued. Our targets were very limited as a result of the depth of the Russian gun pits. We then turned from firing in the direction of the Malakoff where we hoped our efforts had helped the French, towards the Redan. Our men still had to cover around 200 yards of open, rising ground and not just carrying their weapons; as well as ladders this assault wave, known as the forlorn hope as few of them would survive, carried woollen sacks to throw in and thus fill open ditches. Then, if they made it over the ditch the next obstacle they faced was the abbatis. This was a very testing barrier averaging over two yards high and at least a yard wide, filled with felled trees and various uneven lengths of timber with sharpened ends pointed towards the attacking force. Added to this were the constant volleys from the Malakoff to our right, and yet more death and destruction from the left flank of the Barrack Battery.

Survivors then faced having to scale the walls of the Great Redan. If any ladders had managed to be carried over and were then planted at the foot of the walls, then volley after volley was going to rain down on them from above as defenders fired from really close range. It is no easy task scaling a wall on a ladder carrying a rifle and sword. On reaching the parapet, yet more fire was aimed at them from behind barricades by lines of defenders on the opposite side of the redoubt. These defenders on the floor of the gun pit, if they did find themselves being pushed back, could call for help from the men concealed in the tunnels.

The storming party was soon reduced from around six companies, some 700 men, to around one hundred.

It wasn't all failure though; success came to men of the 3rd Division as they broke through into town after driving off Russians from their rifle pits by the Barrack Battery. These men kept driving forward, their momentum taking them on and eventually into the cellars of shattered houses where they found wine, but before long they were forced to retreat.

We, in the meantime, had managed a steady rate of fire into the Redan, but it was soon obvious that the reduced numbers of the forlorn hope could not make any lasting impression on the enemy who were bringing up what seemed a plentiful supply of men. The attack was failing and very soon bugles sounded recall and soldiers turned and ran for their lives, as shots thudded into retreating backs.

That dark cloud of gloom descended once more over the allied camp particularly the English section of it, the Centre. Officers with great difficulty then had to pull their men back to the dull routine of the siege camp. To keep men from thinking or asking too many questions, in most regiments, including my own, they were given the task of trench digging. This rather pointless task was not lost on the likes of Williams though.

"What are we doing, sarge, digging our graves again then we can just be shot, fall in them to save time instead of being killed attacking that bleedin' useless pile of shit?"

"No, just don't want you to feel bored and unwanted," I replied, but at least he had made me smile.

These tasks, after yet more burying the dead and taking the many wounded off to field hospitals had kept the men occupied, nonetheless. We bundled the last of the wounded, a private in the 33rd Foot into a blanket and took him to the surgeon's table. Surgeon Taylor looked haggard, worn out by all the casualties he had been tending. It had been bad for all of us but somehow seeing him there leaning against a blood-soaked table, half-fainting with fatigue, trying to save the mangled remains of a man's arm made me wonder at the point of it all. What had we achieved? It wasn't for lack of trying, on the part of so many men. The gaps in the ranks at morning parade in many regiments was testimony to that.

I had been kept busy with the usual duties expected of a company sergeant. But I was also glad and relieved to return to something that was ordinary and normal like parades, drill, ensuring kit was being looked after and rifles ready for instant use. Order had to be maintained especially after the failure on the 18th.

The newly promoted Captain Axelby, a good choice for company commander, caught up with me three days later and asked me how I thought the men were doing following the attack on the Redan.

"I have noticed disappointment and a general weariness among a lot of them," I said, adding, "usually rifle cleaning is something they do without really thinking about it or having to be told, even though their lives may depend on it. Some men have no enthusiasm and even basic tasks are being avoided. I have had to stand behind a couple of them. Only a few, yet it's not like riflemen to look sullen but they have had a lot to put up with recently, sir."

"Can't disagree with you on that. Others, including Sergeant-Major Reeves have said more or less the same. Keep your eye on things, Finch. We can't afford sloppiness or a collapse of discipline now that we've all gone through so much and are so close to a finish."

I cast my mind back to those dark days of winter and to how low morale had been then. It now looked that the failure on the 18th had really disheartened them. Now they seemed to be plumbing new depths of despair. Duties were performed as though men were walking in their sleep. Exhaustion wasn't helping either and seemed to be making the men very twitchy. I was reminded of rabbits around the cottage at home. The slightest noise made them jerk and look around wide-eyed. Some rabbits just stared ahead or looked so startled with eyes glazed, seemingly unable to move and avoid the pot. So it was with many of the men as they sat staring ahead. Not all of them were capable of playing cards as shells whistled overhead.

One soldier in another regiment had risen during the very early hours, donned boots, his complete uniform and marched off towards the edge of camp. When challenged by a sentry he had levelled his gun at the picket, fired, missed, though the bullet had torn a piece of the sentry's greatcoat. The soldier then ran past the picket line yelling at the top of his voice. Shots were fired at him from the Redan and he then disappeared from view. Several hours later a returning party testing the enemy's strength had found him sitting in a small ravine, sobbing. They brought him back to camp where he was taken before his battalion commander. Several days later he was flogged.

Not too long after this incident he wandered off again and was heard talking to himself. Moments later there was a single shot. He was found with boot and sock off his right foot. Somehow, he had managed to fire his rifle with his toe while holding the muzzle of the gun to his head. I only learned of this from talking to a sergeant in his company. There had been some effort by officers in his regiment to keep the whole thing quiet. The effect on the already low morale might have proved disastrous. As we sat drinking together in Balaklava the whole story was slowly teased out of him.

The French too were suffering. Low morale had led to more desertions, court martial and, so it was rumoured, to the firing squad.

This state of affairs could only get worse if the siege dragged on. What would happen if we had to face another winter? Men from many regiments, including my own, were asking why we were still in the Crimea.

***

Reasons for coming here in the first place to fight the war had never really been properly explained. Even Captain Fortune had been unable to give precise details. Captured Russian deserters also had that same uncertainty though they had often been forced into serving the Tsar and defending Mother Russia. There was an even greater level of ignorance, disaffection and low morale in the enemy's camp. They were probably even worse off than we had been, as we were told stories of food shortages bordering on starvation as well as poor equipment and little ammunition. The Russians to the north of the peninsula were just not able to get supplies through to the town. There were also stories of wounded men lying unattended for days and of casualties being thrown into pits along with the dead. The town of Sevastopol, they said, smelt of death. As the summer temperature had risen, so had the stench from rotting bodies.

The unrest in our camp, which to some of our officers might even lead to mutiny, inspired the issue of another order. Among the many people who seemed to wander through the allied camp was that *London Times* reporter Mr. Russell. Captain Fortune had told me that his reports of how we were suffering hardships during winter and how badly the war had been organised and carried out, had caused anger and consternation at home. It had though, not been very well received in some quarters in the Crimea! Russell did seem much more sympathetic to the men in the trenches rather than towards the senior officers responsible for sending them into battle and for the carnage that followed.

**

Perhaps it had not just been coincidence after all, that matters had begun to improve in food supply and shelter during early 1855.

We had been ordered not to discuss anything with Mr. Russell as whatever we might say and he wrote, could give the Russians information as to our strength and intentions. Both of which they seemed fairly well acquainted with anyway. After all, they could see or hear most of what we were preparing to do; it being quite difficult to hide thousands of men, horses and equipment as they prepared to attack a very well defended position. We were also told to keep clear of another man, Fenton, a photographer. I had seen this man's wagon around the Heights above Balaklava. Photographs I had found very clever and magical, and had been fascinated by the whole process since I had seen my very first ones. On one of my forays in and back from Balaklava I had walked towards his wagon and, prompted by curiosity, had asked him how photographs were made. He showed me inside the wagon. Hanging on small pegs were scenes of battlefields, ships, the harbour below and officers and men from many regiments. He even took my photograph and later on, some of the riflemen and our officers. Photography had, so Mr. Fortune told me, made such an impression on the many thousands who had flocked to London's 'Great Exhibition' in 1851.

This had been England displaying her wealth and strength to the world. We were, according to what Mr. Fortune and now the photographer had said, at the dawn of a new age. Steam had changed the world. What would be next?

***

I had seen a few paintings and daguerreotypes in the Fortunes' house and newspapers contained lithographs, but these photographs were incredible.

Uncertainty of what the next move in the war would be continued. The only sure event was the almost daily bombardment of Sevastopol through the rest of June and into July. We could see Russian casualties from the shelling being taken, when the smoke lifted, by the cartload to what must have been already overcrowded hospitals. That wounded were being added daily to their casualty lists was confirmed by more deserters. How much more could the Russians take?

In May, there had been an attack on Kerch in the north-east of the Crimea overlooking the Sea of Azov. This was to secure that town and give control of whatever attempts the Russians made to send reinforcements south into Sevastopol. The attack had ended in shambles. A joint force of Turks and Tatars had smashed their way through the town. A trail of looting, rape and killing followed in their wake. Things got so bad that a small force of English cavalry was sent to Kerch to restore some sort of order. The town was taken and a garrison including some of my battalion, was left there. As they marched off, members of Captain Axelby's company looked on with some envy. Later on in the month there was another action when an allied force, including Lancers, Hussars, Royal Horse Artillery and Marines, attacked the Russian lines in the Charnaya Valley.

These actions did reduce to a trickle supplies that were reaching Sevastopol. Goods that had come in across the Sea of

Azov were now choked off. Good news for us, but we were still, in July, on the wrong side of the Redan.

Very noticeable was the fact that the Russians were only returning around half of the number of shells that had been whistling in to our lines a few months before. We were managing around 70,000 shells during our barrages. There also seemed, from our observations and that of the French Observer Corps, just military rather than civilians in Sevastopol. Food and water must have been in such short supply that all non-military must have been encouraged to leave. Our constant shelling must have also been acting as quite a persuader.

This could mean that sooner or later they were planning to make a last desperate bid to break the siege and throw us off the Heights before they either starved, or morale dropped so low that they all deserted.

A last effort was soon to take place. It happened under cover of that great ally, fog, on the 16th August. The Russians advanced towards the Traktir Bridge over the River Charnaya. Their force was large, estimated at around 50,000 infantry and 10,000 cavalry with some 250 field guns. All under the command of General Liprandi. After, when the size of their attacking force was relayed to us, I found it difficult to believe that somehow they had managed to put such a force together. Liprandi's men moved to attack the French and the Sardinians.

***

The Sardinians had joined the war against Russia in April and there were around 10,000 of them on the Heights. Many of them wore dark blue, French-style, almost knee-length tunics, with different coloured facings depending on regiment. They also had a blue shako with a black pack, not unlike those worn by the French, and light blue trousers with a red stripe. What really caught our attention among this colourful display when we had first seen them take up their position on Gosfort Hill, were the distinctive-looking battalions of Bersaglieri who wore plumed hats with a broad brim, grey knee-length greatcoats and trousers. With their knapsacks and powder horns they looked more like a large hunting party than soldiers. Nearby, they had light and heavy cavalry and from a distance looked more French than anything.

"Let's hope they fight as pretty as they look," came a voice from our ranks.

They soon faced Liprandi's force while a runner told our company commander that a smaller force of Russians was being kept in reserve. We were told to stand by, just in case!

Fortunately for us all the expedition was badly handled by the attackers' leaders. Their artillery fired too soon and served to warn the French and Sardinians of their approach and position. Although the Sardinians were driven from the hill the enemy could not push the French back. After the battle it was largely agreed that the Russian failure was mainly down to their low morale and hesitation in sending for the reserve force.

***

The eventual attack was half-hearted and before too long Gorchakov ordered a general retreat.

After three days, orders came down that we were to help in the clearing of the dead. By then the stench was almost numbing. Bodies of allied and Russian dead were fast deteriorating in the hot August sun.

Taking a break from collecting casualties, I sat down among the corpses ordering my ten-man detail to do the same. We took the opportunity to take a long drink of warm water from canteens that had also been baking in the heat of the day. I looked across at the devastation all around me as other small groups continued with their grim collecting. Uniforms of grey, blue, both light and dark and many so soaked in congealed blood that it was impossible to tell what the original tunic colour had been, as they all in a macabre way, decorated the field of battle.

I then heard a low moan and there, sitting among all those uniforms, was a Russian officer. He raised an arm. I moved cautiously towards him, remembering the last time I had become involved in helping a wounded enemy soldier. Drawing my sword, I transferred it to my left hand. I managed to roll a few bodies off his legs with my right. As a precaution, I turned to one of the riflemen who were all watching with some amused interest and ordered him to cover the Russian just in case of trickery. The man had wounds to his own legs and shoulder. I offered him my canteen and after a drink from it he handed it back with some difficulty.

He then reached just inside a small pouch attached to his belt and pulled out a golden cross and chain, which he thrust into my right hand. I tried to give it back, but he insisted I take it.

"Merci, monsieur," he said, as I tucked the cross and chain into my sergeant's sash.

I turned to two of the riflemen, "Take this man to the surgeon."

As the two men bundled the wounded Russian into a blanket that fifteen minutes before had been carrying the bodies of ally and foe alike and before we returned to our graveyard duties, I began to think that they weren't that much different to us. They bled and died just as easily.

I turned my attention back to the battlefield. To make the scene even more pitiful, the dead were being stripped of their rings, neck chains and items of uniform. Sickened by this desecration, I ordered my burial detail to fire a warning volley above the heads of the souvenir hunters. They paused, glowered back at us and looked as though they were daring us to lower our aim and fire at them, in the full knowledge that we could not do so. We continued with our task, they continued with theirs.

Their defeat seemed to prompt the Russians into yet another evacuation of Sevastopol. By the end of August they had managed to complete the building of a bridge to the north side of the harbour. Did this mean that they were also, closer to giving up the town or had they merely cleared the town of all distractions and were waiting for us to go in and try and take it from them in one final battle.

From information given to French officers by Russian deserters several days later, they still intended to hold their ground.

This resolve was very evident when during the first few days of September we were told once again to prepare for an assault on the Great Redan. The Russians seemed to sense our plans and shells rained down in great numbers in our direction. Strangely, or so it seemed to me, French confidence as a result of the victory on the 16th August was rising. They seemed rather more prepared and anxious to begin the assault than we were. The walls of the Redan and Malakoff still seemed no less formidable than they had on the 18th June. The French, in their endeavours to get as close to the Malakoff as possible before their attack, had busied themselves digging trenches so close to them that they could plainly hear Russian voices and the tread of boots as the guard changed.

Our attacking force still had that 200-yard death run. We had tried on many occasions to make some impression on the rocky ground to reduce the distance. The enemy once again brought up their sharpshooters to add to the problems our trench diggers already faced. Some of the Russians took up positions in the very few, though very badly damaged buildings, that remained on the southern fringes of the town. Even though their rifles generally lacked the accuracy of our Enfields, the effect of their bullets pinging against the rocks in front of us was particularly unnerving. Our side was also losing around one hundred men each day as that laborious task of trying to add to the trenches continued.

In total command of our army was a new leader, General Simpson. We all hoped that he would give us a better chance of success than Lord Raglan had. Milord Raglan had died at the end of June and, certainly in our camp, was not missed. Where was he when we were frozen and half-starved last winter? In a very warm, comfortable cabin on a ship in Balaklava Harbour.

14

The assault was to take place on the 8th September. This also meant we had a few days to prepare or to worry about the forthcoming attack. Three days before, early on the 5th, our artillery sent in thousands of shells, some from very close range on that day, as well as the two days that followed. Every gun the French had was also brought to bear. Our artillery barrage was so hot that we could see that the enemy artillerymen were just unable to tend their own guns and return fire. If only this could continue as we rushed the Redan!

Even before the 5th there had been some sort of artillery barrage on Russian lines most days. This wasn't merely to deliver death and destruction on them but to keep them guessing as to when the full assault would take place. It would also add to the unsettling and wearing down of the Russians as they were forced to wait, and wait, and worry. From my own experience I felt more tense if a battle was to take place in a few days time instead of being told to just go and get on with it. If the Russians were of a similar mind they must surely be very twitchy. Not that it happened too often the way I would prefer. This obviously had limits, although men of the Rifle Brigade were expected to hold themselves in readiness for anything.

Sometimes it was necessary for additional equipment other than rifles and ammunition to be collected. Kit was always close at hand but ladders, picks, shovels and other scaling equipment might take time to gather. As we fell in all men in my battalion were issued with two days rations.

This in itself was usually a sign that something was in the wind and about to involve us.

At 5:30 a.m. on the 8th September a massive bombardment of the town started, but we were not given the order to move forward. The Russians must have been wondering when the attack would begin. They weren't the only ones! But a strong wind was blowing. This would most certainly have interfered with plans for the allied warships to join in with the bombardment. The strength of the wind was such that ships were being blown around so much that their guns could not be brought to bear on Sevastopol to any great effect or accuracy.

"Stand down, lads," said Captain Axelby, as my company waited in the Quarries. "It seems that General Bosquet has delayed the start of the attack until midday. He wants his men to catch the Russians while they're changing guard. Some of 'em will be grabbing their rations. That's if there's anything left in town for them to eat."

Sergeant-Major Reeves asked, "Who's going to lead their attack? Not the poor bloody Zouaves again, is it, sir?" just as I was thinking why hadn't the general thought about this a bit earlier and save us the trouble of getting ready to go and then being stood down, yet again?

"Yes, it is," he agreed, "but this time the attacking force will be bigger. They're sending five divisions against the Malakoff and the same number against the town."

"When are we likely to go in then, sir?" I asked.

"Well, once the French, yes those Zouaves, will be in the thick of it again, take the Malakoff and raise the tricolour, then it's off we go and in the Redan for afternoon tea."

Once again I thought how easy it all sounded, but then the bugles signalled for the attack to begin. The one, the only advantage the French had was their closeness to the enemy line. Only about thirty yards, or as they called them, metres from the nearest point. Zouaves and the other infantry surged forward towards their objective. Men in the first two waves carried bits of door and planking to fill the ditch and ladders to scale the immense walls of the Malakoff. The plan seemed to be working. The Russians had certainly been caught off guard; very few shots were coming from their defences. Within a few minutes, French soldiers were up their ladders, over the parapet and down into the redoubt. The enemy it seemed, had bolted. Encouraged by this success, the French just kept going. They moved on to attack another position of the Russians left of the Malakoff, the Gervais Battery, then on, heading north-eastwards towards the Little Redan that lay about 500 yards from their first objective.

There they did come across strong opposition, and we were told that French bodies covered the ground as the Russians met their advance with more determination and fixed bayonets. Eventually, French reinforcements caught up with their first waves and the enemy were obliged to fall back.

The scene at the Malakoff was one of frenzied French activity as they prepared to resist Russian counter-attacks. Anything to hand, including the bodies of dead and wounded Russians was thrown up to fill the gaps in the defences. Fascines, large bundles of wood, gabions, cylindrical baskets filled with earth and stones, were pulled from the side that faced the French, and used to block the opposite side of the pit and from where the counter-attacks would come. Then someone on the French side remembered to raise the French flag.

Off we went, but as soon as we rose from our position, Russian guns opened up. The fire was so intense that we were forced to retreat to our starting point. Again, we moved forward. The rocky ground in front as well as the distance to be covered, made this a very perilous undertaking. We faced the roughly 'V'-shaped projection of the Redan, which would be our first point of contact with it. From the arms of the 'V' would come flanking fire. It came in a tempest of roundshot, grape and musket fire that poured into the thousand men of the storming party.

The abbatis was reached, crossed and then we dropped into the ditch.

I moved forward, crouching, with hands clenched around the barrel and trigger guard of my Enfield. The sword was already fixed for the close encounters I'm sure would soon be coming. Again, there was that sick feeling of fear and expectancy of that musket ball or grapeshot that would thud into me. This self-pity left me as I began to urge the men forward.

***

All around me men shouted to give themselves courage to go on. I stepped over bodies as I scrambled over the abbatis. I saw Captain Axelby ahead and to my right, an officer sword in one hand, and his Adams revolver in the other yelling encouragement and urging them out of the ditch and on towards the Redan.

"C'mon, boys, nearly there."

I could barely hear him as more and more of us were drawn into the ear-shattering frenzy of the battle.

Many of the attacking force's ladders had been lost on the way across, and the ditch soon became crowded with men unable to scramble up the walls. Confusion was taking over. Added to this was the concentrated fire from the Russians lined up along the parapets, discharging their muskets into us just below them.

While some soldiers panicked, others did manage to scramble up and over the wall but too many were just falling back dead or badly wounded into the ditch. One of our own officers, I am not sure which one as smoke, bodies, parts of bodies seemed to be falling like a shroud all around, was desperately trying to rally the men of whatever regiment and get them up those few ladders that were leaning against the Redan's walls. I followed his example, holding my rifle in my left hand, I began grabbing at men's tunics pushing them towards those ladders. I don't know how I did it, but I scrambled up a ladder and on to the parapet.

***

Below me I could see that our men were still wavering. A few had retreated to our lines where the second wave waited for the bugle call to send them off. Yet for a very short time we held the Redan, but after the fourth or fifth time of trying the Russians managed to push us back. Below me and in the gun pits of the Redan I could see Russians furiously trying to regroup, but they seemed as disordered as our advanced attack waves were. I just did not have time to take stock of the floor of the Redan littered as it was with bodies and compare it to the times I had seen it from the town side.

The enemy was showing incredible resolve and though short of ammunition with their unreliable weapons they did not look about to give up very easily. They began to throw anything and everything they could lay their hands on in our direction. Stones, pieces of timber, scraps of metal came hurtling towards us. A chunk of stone glanced off my shin and I fell back. This saved my life, for as I fell back I could clearly see it and feel the draught as a shell passed over where a second before I had been standing, aiming my rifle into a mass of Russians not forty feet away.

Other men were fighting as though possessed. I know that some had sworn to take the town this time or die in the attempt. Many, sadly, fulfilled the second, but not the first oath!

From just after midday, when bugle calls had sent us forward, until five in the afternoon, fighting in and around the Redan had been at its fiercest. Hand-to-hand and bloody. Our further progress though was unlikely, and another attempt to retake and secure the floor of the Redan was abandoned.

Codrington, the Light Division's commander, ordered our recall, but not before over 2,000 men had been killed and wounded.

As we had prepared to give the enemy advancing with fixed bayonets another charge to keep them out of the Redan, just before the recall sounded, a large explosion from one of the corners of the position shook the very ground we were standing on. Earthworks, all kinds of debris including bits of bodies were thrown sky high. It seemed that the enemy on the other side of the redoubt were now withdrawing in the hope of drawing us into following them into the town. They had though set the charges too soon, and before we had had a chance to regroup and chase them completely out of the Redan, bugles recalling us had sounded.

As we returned to our own lines, we counted over twenty further explosions like giant firecrackers. Had we not been recalled we would have been cut to pieces.

Later that day there were more bangs, which continued into the evening and the early hours of the next day. From all over Sevastopol there were explosions, but not as a result of anything our artillery had done. The Russians seemed to be doing what the allies had failed to do. We could just make out threads of men, women and children carefully moving over rubble, between blasted buildings and across their battered town towards Fort Nicholas, and then on and over that newly constructed bridge. The final weeks in the town must have been frightening for those non-military people, but now perhaps they could escape.

All around, fires were burning. We could hear the screams of panic and fear. The people walking towards the harbour seemed to be waiting in dread of a possible artillery bombardment against the bridge. One result of this as they began to file across was a strange silence descending on them like a cloak. Perhaps the anticipation of those shells falling on them had made them all hold their breath.

Across the town a thick, black pall of smoke seemed to envelop everything.

Even three days later when we marched into Sevastopol parts of it were still burning. We found an unused bronze cannon, a few stores and about fifty horses, which we took back to our camp a little later. Although at last, in the town we had besieged for a year, we felt little triumph; instead, we just felt relieved.

As we toured the town I came across some familiar houses and streets, though even more damaged than before, and we found thousands of wounded men. They had just been abandoned without dressings, food or water and in desperate straits. Once again, we experienced a shared misery. There were festering corpses, maggots and flies on open wounds. In one hospital, we found that blood had trickled down to the floors below. Where boots had stepped through pools of it, there were red-black smears everywhere. Some men, nearly mad with pain, blackened tongues, twisted limbs and broken bones poking through discoloured skin, looked like those hideous gargoyles that took the water away from the walls of my village church.

Others, our fire having shredded their tunics, sat with blackened bodies.

Among the prisoners, easily captured because they were too exhausted to run away, was a Polish officer. In exchange for a little bread, some dried meat and water he showed us where some of the mines had been buried, but not set off as we had entered the town before their incendiaries could fire them.

We examined the Redan and found around fifty heavy guns. And now that we were not being assaulted by shot and shell had time to look with grudging admiration at other things too. Large guns pointed out and across towards our lines while others were aimed at the Quarries. Halfway down each gun were two large pieces of heavy rope, matelets, completely encircling the barrels to protect their gunners from snipers including those of the Rifle Brigade. As the siege had dragged on, we had found it much more difficult to hit their gunners even though our Enfields were in very capable hands.

The earthworks were a considerable piece of construction. Inside the gun pits, the walls rose six to eight feet from the floor. We knew only too well that the outside of these walls had around a twelve-foot drop to the ditches in front. These walls were so thick and reinforced with stones and earth as a filling and as Captain Bantock had told me, easily able to soak up the heaviest of shells that thudded into them. Then there was the maze of tunnels complete with barrack room under the Redan. This once again confirming much of the information that the captain had collected.

We also realised that although Sevastopol was at long last in our hands, abandoned rather than taken, there were still Russian cavalry, infantry and artillery not too far away. The next few days were a little tense as we waited for a counter-attack to come. It didn't and that mixture of fear and uncertainty began to lift. At the morning parade on 14th September, our battalion commander told us that it did look as though the Russians had, at long last, had enough. But the bad news was that we had to remain on the alert and not resort to drinking in excess in celebration of our success, not to mention to our still being alive after so much suffering. Not that the colonel's plea made too much difference to many men, as over the weeks and months that followed drinking increased and so did fights and punishments. It was perhaps, too much to expect men who had suffered and fought so well not to seek some diversion. Pressure had been released like a cork, from some of those champagne bottles in an officer's hamper from home.

Winter, though, was not going to be the grim prospect that it had been last year. The men had better accommodation. There were huts and not just for sergeants and above. My accommodation had survived quite well though several shell splinters had added to its ventilation.

Shops and bars in Balaklava were full and thriving. There were the usual diversions and amusements sought, and found, by men a long way from home. Men were also making extra money by selling hoarded souvenirs to tourists arriving from England. Officers seemed to look the other way.

**

Perhaps, like me, they thought they deserved a little more after putting up with so many privations. It would also have been very difficult to prevent it. Anything from tunic buttons to icons and swords. So relaxed was the atmosphere now that there was open fraternisation between the allies and the Russians. Odd in some ways but understandable, because, although divided by language, both sides had suffered similar dangers and shortages. There were still a few skirmishes, but it was surely only a matter of time before the door was finally closed on the whole sorry enterprise.

A great effort was being made to bury the remains of soldiers in proper cemeteries. Not only had battles caused large numbers of casualties, but also most of our losses turned out to be from sickness and disease. The French had lost about one in three of their entire force. Ours, overall, had been about one in five.

We also witnessed the mass departure of Tatars from Balaklava to Constantinople and beyond. They feared that if they remained in the Crimean peninsula when the allies left, they would fall foul of the Russians and become the scapegoats for them losing the war. Those two incidents, the cemeteries and the exodus of Tatars, seemed further proof that it would all soon be over.

Then, in late March 1856, came the news that we had all been waiting for. Peace had been finally declared, and three days later on 2nd April, guns were fired to mark the official end of the war in the Crimea against the Russians.

As a final act, English forces were to supervise the destruction of all the docks in Sevastopol. For the French, their symbolic marking of the end of the war was to destroy Fort Nicholas. Before such acts were carried out, the allies moved in and removed a surprising amount of war material, considering how low Russian supplies had been. Our huts on the Heights above Sevastopol were given to the Russians for housing the many townsfolk made homeless. Our artillery had seen to it that there were many such victims.

In July 1856, Balaklava was officially handed back to the Russians.

The last of our army finally left the Crimea on board *HMS Algiers*.

15

In early June 1856, we had marched to Balaklava and boarded *HMS Apollo*. Our return to England passed without incident. By the 13th June, we reached Malta. In the early hours of the 5th July, we sailed into the waters opposite Portsmouth. The morning was sunny and bright.

I leaned against the ship's rail and looked north to the hill above Portsmouth and imagined the scene beyond, towards Romsey and Winchester. Life, no doubt continuing as before, in my village of Lower Durford with the river still flowing.

I could easily get home from here, see the parents I had not seen for more than two years, and get back in time for a special parade I had been given orders to attend.

Leaning against the rail also was Captain Axelby, my company commander. He seemed to be lost in thought as he looked across at the ships busily plying to and fro across the harbour. I moved towards him.

"You look like a man on a mission, sergeant, but with all the cares in the world on your shoulders. But it's over and here we are back home."

It had occurred to me as I had looked north that I was indeed very close to home, only about twenty miles away.

"Yes, sir. Just been thinking about my family and Captain Fortune. We didn't live too far away from each other. Him and his people at the old manor house and mine in the village below it."

"Why not go and see' em then?" he said simply.

"Yes, sir, that's why I've come over to see you. I'd like permission to stop off and see my people. They're about twenty miles away in that direction," I said, pointing past the harbour entrance and to the left of the hill.

"Shouldn't be a problem, Finch," he replied, "after all your loyal service. You've been awarded a special medal, for valour, and I think that allows you a certain privilege. I'll go and see the colonel. Back soon."

And off he went, the son of an earl, asking favours for a lowly village boy!

He returned minutes later, merely adding, "Be sure you're in London by early morning on the 8th July. The rest of us will be in barracks in Aldershot after disembarking and boarding the train from Portsmouth Station. I'll see your kit gets to go with the others attending that special parade."

I thanked the officer, saluted and then managed to catch the attention of a petty officer in charge of a passing jolly boat. A short voyage to a jetty and for the first time in several years I set foot on English soil, well, the wood of the quay. I then caught a train to Southampton and then to Bishopstoke and began the walk home.

As I approached the village of Lower Durford, a brougham drew up by my side. The coat of arms on the door was a familiar one. Then I heard a voice.

"Finch," it said, and an arm beckoned me nearer.

Soon I was face to face with the scarred visage of Lord Durford. He looked much older than I remembered him. His hair was lank, his moustache limp. He looked as though he was giving up on life. There was though, still a touch of acid in the voice but he sounded weary.

"Finch," he repeated, "I understand that you were with my son, James, when he was wounded."

"Yes, sir," I agreed, torn between the thought that I had something he could not know or have in that I was, according to what the surgeon had later said, the last man to speak to his son.

Yet I also felt some discomfort in that I was also the only man with knowledge of the pain that his son must have suffered. I could not inflict that even on this man no matter how detestable I found him.

His son, though, I had respected and would long remember. Yet there was also something else; for some reason, I had always and certainly since joining his company, felt at ease in his presence. But I could not say what it was that made me think that or why he seemed so different. There was never that distance between us that was usual between officers and enlisted men. It remained true that in the Rifle Brigade, divisions between officers and their men was not so clearly drawn. In the field they ate, marched and fought side by side.

In South Africa I was soon promoted corporal, and not long after to sergeant while serving in James Fortune's company. Perhaps this was the reason and not that we were geographically but not socially near neighbours.

"I was with him when he was hit and he did manage to speak." I continued, "He was unconscious when I delivered him to the surgeon. Your son, sir, was, in my humble opinion, a fine, brave officer, respected by his men and a true gentleman."

I could not help myself in adding emphasis to the word, 'true.' *Make of that what you will*, I thought.

"My son wanted you to have this. We found it in his box on its return from the Crimea."

A shaking, gloved hand passed me a small packet tied with string and sealed with wax.

"Thank you very much, sir," I added, very much surprised at this unexpected gift.

Lord Durford leaned back in his seat, called a "Thank you, Finch," and was off as the groom lightly touched the whip to urge the pair forward.

I stood there blinking in the bright, midday sun and still over-awed at the packet and how it had been given to me.

Ensuring that it was firmly in my knapsack, I decided not to go home directly, but instead would go down by the familiar river and pond, which had so captivated me with such interesting views. Soon, I reached my favourite stretch of it and just stood there almost in the exact spot for a few moments thinking back to all the things that had happened since that day. That very special day where I had taken in the soft curves of Lady Sophie.

***

I sat down on a tree stump and reached for the packet. It was addressed to, 'Sergeant John Albert Finch, 1st Battalion, The Rifle Brigade.' I opened the letter and began reading,

Sevastopol,
15th April 1855.

To my very dear fellow and adventurer, Jack,

If you are reading this then it means I've come to a bit of a sticky end, so I'd better put you straight on a few things. You will remember when we were with that engineering chappie that I said there was something you should have been told. I never after that seemed able to find the right moment. Blame the Russkis, but here goes.

My old Pa had a brother, William. Bit of a bad lot I'm afraid. Took more than a liking to many ladies, high and low. Including one of my older sister Georgia's governesses. Mary, I think her name was. Don't know what happened to her.

When the child was born, he was put out to a poor, but honest local family, the Finch's, and brought up as one of their own. So, Jack, you and I are related, some sort of cousins.

I only knew about this because one day I'd fallen asleep in one of those big chairs in the library. You remember the library? I'd be about seven or eight at the time and just before I was sent off to school.

Anyway, Pa and William came in, voices raised. William was in disgrace and he was being encouraged to go away. Off he did go eventually, India I think.

Probably chasing the memsahibs as I write. I was discovered and told to keep my peace and that was that.

That is until a little later when I heard my people talking about shame and keeping quiet about the rutting antics of the black sheep of the family. It seems a poor girl in Romsey Workhouse, not Mary, had died, but not before naming William as the cause of her misfortune. And this was not the first time this had happened. Well, you know what gossips are like, especially in a place like ours. Anything connected with the big house and the wrongdoings there is meat and drink to some people.

Not long after this, for some reason or other it was decided to keep an eye on your progress. Perhaps if rumours did start to fly around about William, fingers might be pointed towards your door. At least, I'd like to think that this was an effort at trying to put right some of William's shameful doings, and his treatment of Mary. If life was hard in your cottage, ways would be found to ensure that food, even coin would find its way down to your family. You may remember delivering bread and other items to the Hall and being told to wait. A secret contribution was also made to provide for your education. Nothing was ever admitted about who your father was and you were brought up, just like any other of the Finch family. It was all a bit of a shock when we first met at the riverbank where, as you know, assorted Fortunes would swim.

Imagine my even bigger shock though when I saw you again. A young man in rifle-green uniform standing in the front rank of my company bound for South Africa.

I was, though, very pleased, but realised that I could not show you any favours. Not that you needed any. You are a good, loyal soldier and what a lark it has been in and out of Sevastopol on our secret visits.

So when you sit, boots off, in front of a roaring fire, toasting your toes to make up for the cold and wet weeks in the Russian winter in some cosy billet somewhere, your wife and children by your side, spare me, your new cousin James a thought, and what might have been Fortunes at war, but in happier times too.

I have left a note with Lieutenant Axelby asking him to retrieve my watch, which I know you always admired, and put it in this packet if the worst should happen. I hope all this is now with you.

At this point, I tipped the contents of the packet out and a small, leather pouch fell into my hand. Inside was the double hunter pocket watch I had seen so many times in such different circumstances. There was a miniature scene painted on the front, Durford Hall I think, and underneath it the initials, J.A.F. *That's odd*, I thought, *my initials*. On the back a small bugle had been engraved and the words, The Rifle Brigade.

I continued reading his letter.

You should also receive a little money sometime.

If you feel up to it, perhaps you could go and see Lady Eleanor and tell her a little about our adventures in the Crimea. Needn't give her all the details though. A bit grim some of it!

I have written to Eleanor saying that one day another man, a very smart soldier in rifle-green might march up to the front door and ask to see her. Don't feel you have to do this, though.

Well, that's about everything. Duty calls. I wish you all the very best of luck in the world.

I am honoured to be and remain, yours truly,
your cousin, James Algernon Fortune.
Captain, 1ˢᵗ Battalion, The Rifle Brigade.

Oh, post scriptum,
She knew you were watching that time at the pond. Knew all the time.

I stopped reading and thought back to what James had said as I had half-carried him back to our lines. I had thought then that he had been delirious or confusing me with someone else. So she had known all along that I had been watching but had said nothing. Perhaps James had confided in her about who my parents were and the fact that we were related as well.

I opened the front of the watch and a lock of raven-black hair tied with white ribbon fell out. The tiniest of notes was tied to it. On it the words, 'To James, keep safe, love Eleanor.' I had seen Lady Eleanor Broughton a few times, but there was one particular time that I now called to mind. There had been a ball at the big house and I had helped with the horses as carriages of every kind had brought guests for the evening's dancing.

From one of the carriages had stepped Lady Eleanor. She was tall, beautiful in a full-length dress, which glittered in the lights from the front of the house. Jewels sparkled in her hair.

I had overheard James mention to a brother-officer that the weddng to Eleanor was postponed until his return from the Crimea. I then opened the back of the watch and out fell a lock of flame-red hair tied with a green ribbon. It bore a similar tiny note, 'To my darling brother, James, love you forever, Sophie.'

I am a soldier used to hard times, having to kill or be killed. I have witnessed the most horrible of sights and the worst that man can inflict on man. Reading this letter of James', with its amazing revelations that answered so many questions and holding his watch and the little notes made my eyes pipe. Something that had not happened in many a long year.

With a very heavy heart I raised myself from my makeshift seat, replaced the watch and contents into the pouch and put it, and the letter, carefully back into the packet and then into my knapsack.

I walked on to the cottage and within minutes there were hugs, kisses, questions and lots of chatter from my family.

After all, too short a time with brothers and sisters and the two people I had always thought of as my parents and always would, took my leave of them promising to return as soon as army duties allowed. I walked slowly away.

I caught the Salisbury southbound train at Romsey. As I did so I was reminded of that day in January 1850, when I had met Fred at Giffard's the fruiterers, and the decision I had made then that had changed my life so much. Then I took the London train from Basingstoke.

I met up with one of my fellow sergeants and he gave me a valise containing a very new-looking uniform. I slipped into the foyer of a nearby hotel and changed.

That morning, the 8th July 1856, was bright and sunny as I found myself standing at attention next to that same Norfolk sergeant I had first met in London six years before. Now we waited for the arrival of Queen Victoria and Prince Albert. Soon a State Coach drove into view and before long Her Majesty was praising and thanking us for our service in the Crimea. She said how concerned she had been over the hardships we had suffered there, and added that she felt confident that if the need arose and other enemies threatened, our response would be just the same.

Later, as we sergeants drank to our health, the Queen and

Prince Albert's health, to those we had left behind and, as the beer flowed to many others, I wondered if it was the right time to look for a change.

Soldiering is, after all, dangerous!